I so hope you enjoy reading my crazy book! I hope that when you read the first few lines, you realise you are reading, what is essentially, the diary of a good friend whose life just didn't go to plan. I keep things real and as a true walking disaster area, I hope every page makes you feel a little better about YOUR life and your journey through it. I have enjoyed writing every word of this as it has made me realise so much about how we can be so unbelievably unkind to ourselves when we don't get things spot on or perfectly correct.

The process has given me so much perspective on how, when faced with true embarrassment, shame and disgrace, choose option 2: Laughter. It really is the only way and definitely the best medicine in the world.

Welcome to and thank you for daring to enter the crazy world of this Menopausal Mayhem Mother.

Much love x

This book is dedicated to SO many people. But I will do my best to keep it as short as I can. You see, when life doesn't go quite as planned and you have to find your way through the fog that leads to a dark tunnel that leads to the light, you need your family and some seriously amazing people around you to hold your hand, make you laugh and believe in you when you don't believe in yourself.

I want to firstly thank my amazing friends : Nichola, who I have known since the dawn of time, she is my sister from another mother and is responsible for so many misdemeanours. Andie, Denise, Lou, Nikki and Paula (there are so many more) for always having my back – you will learn throughout this book I am a bloody liability. I would like to thank ALL my extended family, my cousins and their spouses for always being there through the dark times and the light.

I would like to thank my amazing agent, Tracey Callaghan for believing in me and MAKING me believe in myself.

To the ladies who are known as "Charlie's Angels" whose friendships were most unlikely – my girls' stepmums and one more. Thank you for your love and support. The truth always comes out and it saves people.

To my parents, only one of you is still here, but you have made me so strong and without you and your kindness and endless love I would have folded, no doubt. Mum, oh my darling Mum, I wish more than anything you could be here to read this book.

To my children, YOU are my reason not only for writing this book, but for living. Without you in my life, I would have curled up in that corner and stopped. Thank you for just being magical and YOU. Thank you for accepting the madness, the lunacy and all the embarrassments I have put you through.

To my husband, you saved us all in so many ways, but if you ask me once more if I could tidy my office you will end up under the patio.

To my wonderful followers on Facebook and Instagram – thank you for believing in me too. Thank you for your love and support.

But this book is mostly dedicated to my Mum. I still cannot believe you are gone, I don't think I ever will. You were quite simply magnificent and I adore you.

Credits :
Amazing photography by www.jennysmithphotography.co.uk
Fantastic artwork designer : Emma Jayne Creative

The Confessions of The Menopausal Mayhem Mother

By Emma Skeates

Chapter 1 - The best laid plans go to waste

Two blue lines.

I am married to a man who doesn't love me, doesn't come anywhere near me... and yet, two blue lines.

How in God's name... Oh my God, that's it, the second coming... Ah, perhaps not; a virgin was required at the last little immaculate conception and well - let's just say I enjoyed my 20's. Ok I made some hay in my thirties too, so that's completely out of the question.

He hasn't come near me for months, how in the devil's name (moved away from divine intervention to something far more sinister) has this happened? Then those dreaded flashbacks from a drunken night on my birthday start to emerge. We had only been married a few months and it was clear that he had realised almost immediately that he'd made a monumental mistake. All my fault of course, I hadn't QUITE warned him of what a walking catastrophe I was. The honeymoon was a disaster, I'm not exactly Elle Macpherson and she seemed to be there with a different head all over the place which didn't exactly help matters. I'm more of a Mrs Bean really, falling in the pool after one too many cocktails on the first night then arising like a drenched Alice Cooper, in front of all the Elle doppelgangers. My new husband's look of horror was probably the first sign that things weren't quite going to pan out quite as I had hoped.

But after many months of walking around each other like two caged tigers, there they were, the two blue lines. I had always wanted the white picket fence, the 2.2 children and the Volvo on the drive, I just hadn't quite pictured it all starting out like this... but they say all trouble starts with fabulously laid out plans so I went with it. I didn't exactly make pregnancy look easy. No, I do believe that self-pity itself looked down on me with embarrassment and said, yep, you've taken me to the extreme.

As the birth of this alien-being (that had been kicking the crap out of me) loomed ever closer, the more terrified I became of the fact that there was in fact going to be a baby emerging and I had NO idea what on earth I was going to do with it. There I was; failing so badly at being a wife (I didn't play for Arsenal, what can I say) and I was going to have something that weighed hopefully only about the same amount as a watermelon attempting to be pulled out of a hole the same size of my nostrils. THAT was not what was scaring me. A baby, a real live baby that was going to depend on me, the girl with the opposite of The Midas Touch, everything I touch turns to broken. How on earth was this ever going to work?

Laying on the operating table awaiting my C-section, the lovely registrar asked me what I would like them to do with the baby once "it" was born.

"I'm sorry, I don't understand the question?" was my reply.

"Well, would you like us to hand the baby to you and put it to your chest to let you bond with it immediately? Or alternatively we can check the baby over and then bring it to you, the choice is yours?"

I had a choice! Oh the relief!

"Um, I don't think I've really thought this through, sorry, can I go back and not actually have a baby. You could take it away and dress it and see how it feels, and then when it's old enough to know if it wants a parent who has not got a feckin clue what to do with it, then could we have a rethink?"

It turns out that Angelique, the beautiful registrar, had never come across this reaction before and gave my despairing husband a look of "shit, you can deal with this one". He stuttered into life (I think this was the first time I had actually heard him speak in about 6 months).

"Oh, um, just get the baby out and then clean it up a bit and I will talk to Emma, she will be fine, leave her to me".

They warned me of the unbelievably strange sensation of "a washing up feeling in your belly" whilst they pulled your baby out of the sunroof. You have no pain but no amount of warning could have prepared me for the sheer panic I felt as they rummaged around for my future child and I was only just realising that I was really going to have an ACTUAL baby.

Suddenly this grey, statue-like being was carried over my head and taken to a platform and wrapped in a towel. I felt nothing. Blank, emotionless, nothing. Then she screamed. That was it, she didn't exactly say my name, but it was the moment in my life that changed me forever. I was no longer me, no longer Emma, the useless failure who got absolutely nothing right, I was that little girl's everything and she needed me. I felt a huge shiver run through my lifeless body, part of my soul left and another huge one entered, altering me for the rest of my life, and I knew it.

"BRING HER TO ME!!!"

The relief around the room of the anaesthetists, nurses, Angelique but most noticeably my husband was tangible. They brought this strange looking little thing and laid her on my chest and what I felt at that moment is indescribable love. Everything changed forever. I would never be me again. They say that when a baby is newborn that people often liken them to one or the other parent. The truth is that all newborn babies look like potatoes. But this was MY potato and I was completely and utterly in love.

So my new love affair began and even though the marriage was, well like flat coke really, a huge non-event, nothing mattered but my beautiful little Abbie. She was my world. Which was just as well really because I don't think I got any sleep from then until well, until never really. Although I loved this little being with every nerve and fibre in my being, I did have to lock myself in the downstairs loo a couple of times to prevent me from trying to do a perfect drop kick through the nursery window and score my 3 winning points and a good night's feckin sleep. It was during this period of what everyone else describes as "temporary madness" (I will expand on that later) that it dawned on me that my husband and I had still not actually had a conversation since we tied the knot.

We spoke, sort of, exchanges of information, 'pass the salt' etc. Even on the odd memorable occasion there was an actual greeting, but other than that, we really were ships that passed in the night (me being rather more an aircraft carrier, which might have been the reason for his disinterest). I started to overthink about this, I started to wonder if this baby, this beautiful, screaming and fascinating little being could have brought us closer together... but then in a brief moment of lucidity I remembered moments such as 5AM, a Tuesday morning I think it was, I heard him coming down the stairs shouting:

"Jesus, Emma, is there a cow in the house?"

Alas, no, it was me, 4 stone heavier than when he married me, hair like an ageing rock star, make up actually under my nose (it was the day before yesterday that it was still under my eyes) with an electric breast pump attached to my newly found udders - which SO cruelly and ironically sound just like a moo-ing heffer.

I saw it, right there, the look he had been desperately trying to hide since the day we married, a look of pure revulsion. He knew the mask had slipped, so he apologised and walked upstairs to try and work out why he had married a Friesian rather than a Swede. I had to face up to it, I had let myself go, to complete dereliction. Time for action.

Thursday: make up raised to eye level, frock on (ok maternity but he would be used to that by now), soft lighting (hide the size, shape and general demeanour of a woman on the edge) and a smile frozen on my face that I thought the mud might crack behind my ears.

"She needs a sibling!" Strange opening for the first conversation in ooh, 18 months.

"Ah, ok, yes, you are probably right. Can you let me know when you are next ovulating and I will see what I can do..."

Hmmmm, not quite the response I was expecting but it wasn't a complete stomach gag reflex and 'you've got to be kidding me?' neither.

"Well as luck would have it, I am ovulating now actually." Ok, so there was the gag reflex.

"Ok, well, Arsenal are playing at 19:30 so could we talk about this at half time?"

Once again, there was no actual vomit, no actual 'you really are kidding me now aren't you?' it was just a mere reluctance.

But good to his word, at half time he came upstairs, he undressed and before I could say "what shall we call it if we conceive", it was all over, bar the tapping of the watch face...

"Second half..." and he was gone.

Two blue lines. There they were again. I couldn't believe it. It really was almost an immaculate conception, I certainly didn't feel the physical contact? How could this be? But it was and 9 months later little Jaime appeared, another little perfect potato to add to my mash.

Things jiggled along for a while, no actual conversation or certainly any physical contact but with a newborn baby and a toddler who overnight hates you because she thinks you've replaced her with a smaller potato, I think I actually found that comforting rather than worrying. Which was why the only meaningful piece of information that he gave me during those rather long, tedious 3 years was the morning before the Easter bank holiday. He set off for work, nothing unusual, just shouted goodbye from the front door and scarpered. Only today he called, about 30 minutes into his journey.

"Emma", (this was an enormous relief, he DID actually remember my name!)

"Yeah hi, you ok?"

"Um, yes, but I'm not coming back."

I have to admit, I was unshocked, unsurprised.

"Shit, is the traffic that bad on the M25?"

The pause that followed was somewhat lengthy, approximately a month long, or at least it felt that way.

"Uh no, Emma, I am not coming back, *ever.*"

SHIT, the traffic can't be THAT bad! Then, ever so slowly, my reality, my new life as it was to be, dawned on me. How did I not see this happening? How did I not know? But I didn't and that was when everything went black, and when I came to, the colours of my world were dimmer, less bright, life was darker than it had ever been.

Chapter 2 - Divorce and the beginning of unsupervised mayhem

So, months had passed. Divorce solicitors picked over the bones of my marriage and all the while, I had to be a mother, a happy, joyous, entertaining mother to a 5 month old baby and toddler. This was done mainly hungover and with the help of some seriously good friends and family. Then the wonderful day came where we had finally sold the marital home and we were heading back to where I grew up, where I was a small child, in a normal, unbroken, nuclear family. I was going home and it was Independence Day. No it really was, July 4th and I have never felt so scared and yet so relieved at the same time.

Here we go, a life plan turned on its head and a future that was so uncertain that both excited me and terrified me, as it came with a brand new stamp across my forehead 'Single Mother. Broken Family'. But with that self-inflicted stigma, with no money, no plan, no stability, I had replaced despair and loneliness with something so much more valuable, something that kept me going through the next sometimes agonising, mostly hilarious few years, that thing is called "hope".

I woke up on that first morning in our new home, our place of safety, a place where he didn't have a key to access our space at any given moment, and the sun was shining. The view was nothing spectacular but I knew that that morning, even though my heart was still full of fear and my world was still a washing machine that was on an endless cycle, that there was no-one else in that little village who had woken up to the colours of their world slowly returning. I smiled, for the first time in months, from within myself and I said out loud:

"Emma, you can do this."

And at that precise moment, I knew I could. I don't think it was some kind of deep and meaningful epiphany, I think it was the realisation that I had no feckin choice. There I was, equipped with everything that I needed, two small children dependent on this accident prone, disaster area for all their needs and the only thing I was lacking was self belief. But my reality was, I had no choice. It was to lie in a corner and die, or breathe in, then breathe out and repeat.

Emma had arrived at her new life. She was a divorced single mother of two and she HAD to make this work. Self pity was not an option. I had had the most idyllic upbringing with two amazing parents, I had no time to lick my wounds, the nervous breakdown would have to be put on hold and I was going to give my girls the same experience that I had, with one little added ingredient. A little madness...

So you see, in these situations, you actually have to start somewhere. You have to make a beginning and I chose to put some food in our cupboards. Good plan. We all need to eat. Ok, I have done this a hundred times before, on my own, but never with the 'Fat Fucken Failure' stamp on my forehead. But hey, would that make my experience any different? Only one way to find out. Pile the little tikes in the car. Abbie had got to that wonderful stage where she became a rod of steel whilst trying to get her into the car seat, jeez, that girl was going to have a serious inner core when she was older, both physical and metaphorical. The screaming that went with the resistance drew quite some attention from my new neighbours which was not the start I really wanted.

Once I had managed to bend my 2 year old in half and force her into her car seat, I went in and got Jaime and strapped her in. Hey, this was going well! Slam the ol' banger into reverse and apart from the enormous clunk and crunch I thought I'd done ok. Of course I hadn't, as I had in fact run over the only pushchair that I had. So, now equipped with two pushchairs, that is two halves of one pushchair, I surreptitiously hid the broken remains of my only other form of transport in the garden and headed off to Tesco undeterred.

Somehow managed to get both little ducklings in the trolley with no major disturbances and headed off around my new playground. It may sound strange to me calling a supermarket that, but one thing you discover very quickly as a single parent, is that most of your life is under house arrest, so a trip to the supermarket is actually something that is almost for you, not for your offspring. Trips to the swings and toddler groups were definitely not my idea of adult fun but choosing groceries and planning meals for one and liquidised meals for two was a real treat, like daytime clubbing!

As this rather tragic realisation dawned on me that I valued a Tesco shop as a 'treat', I had already reached the dairy aisle. It was a bad moment. A sad moment. If only it had stayed that way... You see I grew up in this lovely Sussex town and there, in front of me, was my very first crush. John Stanley, as I live and breathe. He hadn't aged, hadn't really changed but it was like a trip in the tardis for me, I was 16 again. I, of course, had never told him how deeply in love with him I had been back then. I had just been one of his mates and hung out with him at break and lunchtimes, smoked my way through a pack of 10 JPS to impress him... until he fell in love with a girl 2 years older than me and broke my heart *and* left me totally addicted to cigarettes.

But none of that mattered now, there he was. As you will learn, as you get to know me, I don't do anything particularly conventionally or sensibly. I like to make people remember me in some way so my decision to skulk up behind John and pinch him rather firmly on his arse. This pinch was evidently rather more firm and in fact painful than intended and the poor man fell headlong into the milk rack - which was surprisingly deeper than you would think. All would have been fine, except for a rather nasty case of mistaken identities, not in fact John Stanley at all, just a poor man, out for a pint of milk, getting randomly attacked by a deranged single mother with no colour in her face whatsoever. Pulling him out was no mean feat either, a terrible old tangle of legs and metal racking and as luck would have it, a few bottles of semi skimmed had burst as well so he was also soaked in milk and bruised.

What do you say? Does:

"Sorry about that!"

even vaguely cover what you have just done? It most certainly doesn't explain it. I was greeted with a look of confusion, crossed with pain, anger and astonishment. However, that was displayed across this poor man's face was utter fear.

I'd give it a go.

"So sorry about that. I thought you were someone else!"

Nothing. Still fearful, still very very wary.

"You see, I'm not getting a lot of sleep at the moment so I get easily confused, I thought you were someone who I really wanted to get off with years ago, but you're not him and that's not your fault and I am so so sorry that I pushed you into all that milk."

I was scaring myself now. He just looked like he would do anything, and I mean, anything, to be anywhere else but right where he was at that precise moment. He just raised a gentle hand which was easily understood. Back away, Emma, back the fuck away. The next thing I heard was the Tesco tannoy system:

"Colleague announcement, can a TC cleaner please go to the dairy aisle, a man and a lot of milk need cleaning up."

Then I am sure I heard the tail end of a little laughter. There was nothing more I could do, I had done enough in fact. So, I made all three of us very scarce and flew around the store at a great rate of knots and disappeared back to my prison cell of safety where I couldn't harm anyone else. Not such a great treat to myself as it turns out, just mortification and a Google search for the next closest supermarket to our new home.

Getting the kids into the house without anyone seeing us was of the utmost importance. I knew if I saw any of the lovely village people and if anyone was vaguely kind to me, which invariably they all always were, I would have dissolved into a large pile of tears and ended up as a huge puddle of self pity on the drive. I decided I would do that in the privacy of my tiny hallway which as luck would have it had lipstick footprints walked all over it, as Abbie had spent most of the car journey home rifling through my handbag... finding my red lippie and had coloured in the soles of her new boots and had of course paraded through my newly rented home leaving some really quite artistic patterns. You always think when watching a sad film when people drop to the floor in despair that it is all for dramatic effect. I can assure everyone that this is not the case. This is the moment when you have quite simply run out of all energy, all human strength. If you take one more step you are falsely saying to the world,

"I can do this, I'm ok, it's ALL going to be fine".

No, falling down the wall is a moment that I think comes to almost ALL parents at one point in the week or another, where you actually have to stop the world, quite simply because you want to get off. You need to press pause, have stillness, calm, and breathe. Tragically, unlike in the films, that moment does not last for an eternity with beautiful, heartbreaking violin music. In the real world, in my world that moment lasts for less than 2 seconds when you get pounced on by a 2 year old who is dying to tell you that the whole house has been burgled by someone with red shoes!

Two options, that is all there is at that point in time. Curl up in a small, foetal shaped ball and be kicked around the house by guilt and defeat or, option two, get up; nothing elegant, you can in fact make your way at this stage on all fours, that is part of the choice of option 2, but you get up. You put one hand, then knee in front of the other and you make the next hour happen. It's rare you remember how you did it, but autopilot is something that I found, deep within my mind that saved Abbie, Jaime and me from certain domicide. Then there is wine.

Chapter 3 - Things that seemed like a good idea at the time

It's Wednesday, somewhere a few months after that ecstatic Independence Day and my life seems to be turning into a series of 'things that seemed like a good idea at the time.' I used to joke that was the actual definition of a husband, but the joke was on me because it really was what I had made the definition to be. Last night's 'cheeky cheer up bottle of plonk' was another example of that. Oh, come on Emma, what harm can it do and anyway, you've had a shit day.

You copped a Clarks shoe in the nose whilst forcing a rigid toddler kicking and screaming into a car seat, pushed a complete stranger into a milk crate in a huge supermarket and spent the best part of 2 hours scrubbing a carpet that will never belong to you clear of 'kiss me quick scarlet' lipstick. That first glass barely touches the sides but with the second halfway down the hope replaces the despair and even the sound of small children chiming-

"Mummy!" every 3 minutes seems to bring a smile to your face rather than grasping great handfuls of your own hair.

That is why ALL, well ok, MOST mothers of young children drink wine. To make the agonising hours from tea until actually sleeping children (these are often interminable) not only bearable but vaguely amusing and enjoyable. Their lives depend on it some nights. But the following morning, it is always, without a shadow of a doubt, something that seemed like a good idea at the time. There is no time for regret or hangover, there is only a repeat of the day before, and the day before that, and the one before that. So, you make a renewed vow, that today WILL be different.

Today I WILL be a fabulous mother and I WILL be happy and fulfilled and NOT feel like a total failure at every aspect of my life. Thank the Lord I did all the shopping yesterday... except for the milk. Shit shit shit. No milk. Ok, panic not, no need to hit that wretched supermarket again, we have a wonderful garage on the other side of town where no-one knows me and they sell milk.

CBeebies was swiftly switched off, kids bundled into the car and off we headed. This is going well, no tantrums, no crying, I look at the passenger seat and I've even remembered my handbag, this is fabulous. My headache isn't even too bad. Things were finally looking up and I was NOT in fact the walking disaster that I had now had tattooed across my forehead. I was smiling, oh my god, I was actually smiling. The sun was out and everything was going to be ok.

Life was like that, small things can make you feel wonderful and even smaller misfortunes can send you into the depths of despair. It's the price you pay for living one day at a time, refusing to look at the big picture and what the future holds.

Run into the shop, purchase the milk, with YES YES YES, my wallet! I remembered my wallet. This was all too much. Upon exiting the forecourt shop, I jumped into the car and instantly felt there was something slightly amiss. Ah, I knew it, this was too good to be true A timid, lady's voice said:

"Hello there."

There it was. Reality. This picture wasn't right. But for some reason my instant reaction was to sit quietly behind the wheel of the car and take stock slowly and breathe. After what felt like hours, which of course had only been seconds, I looked to my left and there sat a very smart, really smiley lady with a distinct look of... hmmm, what was it... yes, indeed it was, pity in her eyes. I replied very quietly-

"Hi. I'm in the wrong car aren't I?"

I felt my breath quicken with that awful falling feeling of, no, not again. Very, very slowly, in order not to raise too much alarm, I looked to the car to my left which contained my two little girls staring at me from their car seats. Funnily enough, they didn't look scared, or in any way surprised (they had learned from an extremely young age, that their mother wasn't quite, how shall I say, normal and that their upbringing would in fact involve many more of these awkward situations).

"Please tell me it is at least a similar model and colour to my car?"

"Take a look love, oh and don't mind the husband, he laughs at everything".

I couldn't understand why she wasn't in more of a panic. I was a stranger, I had entered her vehicle, got into the driver's seat. I could have been a violent hijacker, so why was she so calm and yes, there it was - she was actually amused.

I very gingerly got out of the car and stood back to see that I had in fact got into a top of the range, black Mercedes estate, which was neatly parked next to my bashed up bright blue Astra. I was still wearing my pyjamas and my dressing gown. Her husband was at this point on his haunches having some kind of 'episode'. Ok, he was helpless with laughter which made the whole incident even more excruciating. I thought things couldn't get any worse until I spotted all the Shell staff had witnessed the whole event and were also enjoying my embarrassment to the full.

Never has a drive off a forecourt been so painful. I have done the walk of shame more than once where I have accidently put diesel in a petrol engine and had to wait for the AA etc, that had nothing on this. I had wanted a discreet little half litre of milk, no-one would notice the PJ's, it was almost dark. The worst part? They were Hello Kitty pyjamas... I was 38 years old.

Chapter 4 - Never underestimate the power of being an idiot

The morning began with, as it always does with small children, about 5.30am. Despite my agonising embarrassment from the day before, I felt strangely invigorated and thought, today is not just one day, it is in fact, day one! Wow, where in heaven's name did I get this kind of positivity and energy from? It either spelt an amazing turn around from the black fog that had enshrouded my thoughts for the past year or so, or indeed, as it was me, it could just be highly hazardous! I got the sprogs dressed, jollied them into the car, crowbarred Abbie into her car seat and off we headed to the beach. December, and we headed off to the beach. Perhaps my sanity really was beginning to return and all the more recent mishaps were just the fog of postnatal madness, divorce and a house move all thrown into one. So, with children beautifully and rather elegantly, I may add, crowbarred into their car seats we headed off for the coast.

Wow, we can do this! I feel alive, I feel positive, I feel adequate... I've forgotten the beach hut keys. Oh sod it, it's not that cold!

Of course, coldness is all relative really. -4 degrees for example with a windchill factor of another -10 makes for a bracing and sort of numbing experience. Initially Abbie and Jaime seemed to just love the idea of having the freedom to just run around a load of shingle at breakneck speed.

You always think, watching your beautiful children run on a beach having been cooped up in a tiny two up two down for several days would be an emotional, even uplifting experience, which I am sure it was looking back on. Ah, who am I kidding. I had lost all the feeling in my nose (which is sadly a rather prominent figure on my face) and it was now dripping. My legs were starting to feel like they didn't exist and as luck would have it, the only vaguely warm part of my body, namely my head, which was enshrouded in a really warm and very not fetching beanie.

This was to join my frozen extremities as the bastard thing blew off and suddenly became something that resembled the dancing plastic bag from one of those arty farty movies without the arty fartyness. Shit fuck bollocks, I now had a few decisions to make. Catch the bastard hat or maintain some sort of dignity as two rather fetching surfers were walking up the beach. Jeez, I need to be able to feel my head or God only knows what will happen to these two little people over the next hour or so. So off I went, at full tilt, all 70 kilos of loveliness racing across a shingled beach into a raging and freezing easterly wind in hot pursuit of a really knackered old beanie. Apparently, this was not only a sight to behold for the surfers but my offspring as well because, whilst trying to keep one eye on them, I was not entirely focused on my onward path and was indeed heading for a wooden breakwater which had been there my whole life, I just appeared to have forgotten about it.

You see, I was fortunate enough to have been brought up by my gorgeous parents on this very beach with this beautiful beach hut. I just don't seem to remember my mother making such an absolute twat of herself as I was about to do. So, here we all are, time is standing still for a moment, sadly my sizable derriere is not. The beanie is like a kite with no strings, I am a large unit racing extremely unsteadily at a strange angle across the shingle, the kids are staring at their mother as even they can see the inevitable and the surfers appear to be slightly confused as to where they have come out of the sea into a parallel universe where some strange pantomime is taking place... and there it was, the hit. It's remarkable really how quickly you come to a halt when greeted by a wooden structure designed to hold back the power of nature, and by this I am not referring to my enormous frame, but the entire body of the English channel. It was quite an extraordinary display looking back. As I had entered my engagement with this seaweed and barnacle covered wooden pole, I was at quite a strange angle, I hit the horizontal part of the wood with my left breast and the vertical part with my un-beanied head. Bang, out cold.

It turned out that what I had managed to create from my very non arty farty beanie chase was something far more poignant and realistic. I was in fact a perfect, if not enormous, starfish on the stones. I stared at that black sky for seemed like an eternity until four extremely angelic faces began to peer over me.

Oh dear God, I was dead. Who on earth was going to make sure Abbie and Jaime got their doorstep sandwiches? What the feck was going to be written in my obituary:

"She was sadly lost, at some speed by a South Coast breakwater, no-one is really sure what the feck she was doing, it was an odd way to end it all".

Then I started to realise that I was actually breathing and one of the angels was indeed talking to me,

"Mummy, why are you lying in a load of seaweed?"

The silence that followed was endless. Until it ended of course when one of the older cherubs muttered-

"This is your mother? What was she doing?"

Abbie then proceeded to do what all small children do best, tell the truth and reveal everything.

"Oh don't worry, she does this kind of thing all the time. She sometimes even pushes other people over in the supermarket. I think it makes her feel better about how much she falls over herself…"

Right, that's it, I am fully awake and back in my world of mortification and mayhem. Getting up was slightly slower than the realisation that I was in fact alive and not living an out of body experience, I was very much in my own body and now had to try and render it vertical with some semblance of elegance. Nah, never going to happen. One of the beautiful, young surfers who was seriously knee tremblingly gorgeous, took my hand and with every ounce of that beautiful torsos strength, gave this middle aged woman one enormous yank. He got a bit of leverage but not quite enough to stop us from both ending up back in the same heap of seaweed that I had lived, died and lived again in. It took his mate and the two kids to pull us both up and out of the green slime.

What on earth do you say? It is your only interaction with anything resembling a 'man' for many months and you have seaweed hanging off your hair that has been slightly more than windswept. Your resemblance to Medusa is far too close and the only explanation you have for what has just happened is on the other side of the breakwater floating away like a large, flea ridden tea cosy.

Nothing for it, start talking shit. Relentless, meaningless shit as it turns out and pretty unstoppably. I think the crying at the end might have finished the poor lads off as they also started to back away after a few minutes of meeting this interminable loon. Oh God, I really can't go anywhere.

So, heading back to the car, because it is not in fact the children who are frozen to death having fallen in a rock pool but their mother, the shame and dark cloud descended once more. Will I ever get this right? Will I ever rise above this utterly shit situation that I have found myself in.

I mean, really? Can things get any worse? I have learned in this strange journey that I began against my will, that that question never quite turns out to be JUST a question, it offers a challenge to the universe that should possibly be left to challenge someone else. Someone slightly better equipped. It was that day that I learned I had been heartlessly replaced.

Chapter 5 - In steps reality

The one thing that you learn when your life spins out of all your control is never to say

"Right that's it, I've got this licked."

It turns out that this works in your favour too, as the whole truth that nothing ever stays the same, is a good thing. On returning from my disastrous trip to the beach I had the pleasure of calling my soon to be ex-husband having found a message on my machine saying he would like to talk to me about the children. So with a heavy heart, I rang his number. I think the reason I dreaded these phone calls was that there was always a small amount of ridiculous optimism that he was actually going to say that he had made a dreadful mistake and had run into a breakwater somewhere far more exotic, sustained a head injury that had made him fall out of love with me... but he had now come to his senses and realised that I was not a disgusting incubator who held no attraction for him whatsoever, but that he had come back to the idea that I was his one and only and we would go back to being the... oh hang on, we were never a happy family. Optimism gone, phone call just a phone call, or so I thought... The sound of the usual ringtone, but this time a lovely female voice answered the phone.

"Ah, hi there, sorry, I think I must have dialled the wrong number."

"Who is it that you are looking for?" she asked gently

"Oh it's my children's father, he lives alone, sorry to have bothered you".

"Are you looking for Mike?"

It's extraordinary, when you really do get a shock and people say you stop breathing, you do. For a moment, the only thing that told me I was still alive was the pounding in my chest. It was the only thing I could hear, or was it the only thing I wanted to hear. I didn't want to hear her say his name again.

I didn't want to hear the person that I wanted to be saying anything really. But what do you do? There are no breakwaters to throw yourself into, there is no way of stopping time and making sure that you have not just changed your entire, ridiculous fantasy of hope. It has happened and you have to say something.

"Um. Yes. Mike."

"Is that Emma?"

I don't want to be Emma, please please let me be anyone but Emma. But I am her, I am the loser here. I lost everything, and I think it's to you, but so far we are only establishing who I am. Here goes.

"Yes, this is Emma, I am Mike's wife."

I can't be sure, but I think she had her own breakwater moment right there, right then. Did she only hear the heart beating and nothing else. If she did, she didn't give it away. She sounded calm, too calm and just simply said,

"Let me get him for you, Emma."

I can't do this. I can't talk to this stranger. But he's always been a stranger, I had just managed to delude myself for so long that this was not real, that my life was on hold and suddenly, the next few minutes, someone was about to take their finger off the pause button. I wasn't ready to be woken up, to be stirred from my peaceful, painless coma of pretence. No choice, here it was again, the inevitable wave of pain.

"The kids are fine, I have a head injury, but they are ok. Who was she?"

I practically sang that whole sentence like a monk would sing monotonically his chant.

"Oh that's a friend of mine, she stays sometimes. The girls have met her."

What, who is this person that my children have told me nothing about. There was only Chris that had popped over a few times, they had mentioned him, but no bloody family friend woman type person?!

"What's her name?" Not singing anymore, slightly shouting in fact.

"Now calm down, Emma, her name is Chris and we have known each other for years."

Oh now the pain is actually hurting, physically. I think it's in my right shoulder, yes, it is going down my arm. Shit, it is getting worse, holy mother I am having a bloody heart attack! I am going to die, because of a bloke, a woman called Chris! Ah no, in fact, had started running the hot tap and had left my right arm in the water flow and was now getting third degree burns.

"Shit, Mike, I'm sort of on fire, I will call you back."

I restarted the phone call with-

"I need to meet her, Mike, she spends time with our children, I want her to know me and I want to know her."

"Ok, but do I have your word that there won't be a scene?" - his only concern. He had shattered my world once before and without any anaesthetic he was doing it again and yet appearance and calm were his only priority.

"No, absolutely, no, no scene. The children will be there. I just want to meet her."

"We will come down together when I collect the children tomorrow."

"Fine."

And that was it. The start of a story that shaped so many lives. The real start. The real ending. It was tangible, the change in my world. I couldn't initially work out if it was pain or relief that I felt as I walked back into my world of two tiny children and my little safe haven. Was I safer now? Or was I in fact only really facing the true sense of single motherhood? I knew that only time would tell and I had to take one step at a time. But this was me, and I was not going to be told how to feel or how to think. I was going to call my friend and we were going to drink wine! Isobel had always been my rock.

Even though she was maid of honour at our wedding, she almost threw a jubilant punch in the air when she heard he had left me.

"Never liked him. Dodgy hair."

"And you are telling me this now?!"

"Yeah, it's the rule of friendship, watch your mates make cock ups, just make sure you're there to pick up the pieces when the whole thing comes crashing down"

My goodness, she was there. Always armed with some new alcoholic beverage which her PR firm was sampling and so the party would begin. My darling parents would be commandeered to have the children for the evening and Izzy and I would put the world to rights, mainly with a good old moan which would then accelerate pretty fast into us donned with Russian hats cavorting around my living room to *Dancing Queen*. On this particular occasion, we chose Steve Harley and Cockney Rebel and *Make Me Smile (Come Up and See Me)* – a song that would come back to haunt me later on. But that night, it positively saved me as did Izzie.

Well that seemed like a good idea at the time. Good god, at one point between bottles, I had moments of brilliance and true joy about the future of my existence. Why can't we take that moment and bottle it. Oh, yes of course, someone already has, it's called Rioja and it gives you a banging headache the next day along with a head full of regrets and guilt.

So, I had done myself in, I looked like utter shit and I had to meet my replacement. Chris. Chris. Chris. It's a fucking man's name! The kids had talked about Chris the neighbour, who always played with them, he sounded lovely, almost effeminate in some of the things he would get up to with them.

Playing with dolls, painting their nails, dressing them up with his wigs... oh for fuck's sake, Emma, how did you not see it?! Apparently not because you were about to meet Christina, the new model. I hope she has thighs that could kickstart a jumbo. Oooh, good, here comes the nasty bitch inside of you, haven't heard from her for a while. Must drink more, this brings out your fighting side. Right, upstairs, wash hair, put on slap, look... like a drag queen with a massive hangover. Ok, just do your best, practise your worst fake smile and try to look piteous. She will be feeling jubilant and will have the moral high ground and you will once again be wearing your big old head stamp 'VICTIM' - so you may as well look the best victim you can muster.

The children, of course, were vile all morning. Jaime decided to tip her breakfast all over her head minutes before their father and *Chris* were due to arrive. He had a thing about the girls being immaculately presented. I just had to hope that he liked Cheerios and milk on a pair of pink dungarees a size too big. Abbie had decided that hiding in the cupboard under the stairs was always a good idea, so my beautifully choreographed welcome was actually one small baby wearing a bowl of cereal (and little else) and me, also cheer-ioed up, looking positively Joker-like shouting desperately for my eldest daughter who was seriously brilliant at hiding.

There it was, the doorbell. It was a small miracle that I could actually hear with all the screaming and shouting that was going on in my little house, and that was just me, the kids had gone totally silent, especially the missing one. Oh fuck it, in for a penny... I opened the door to be greeted by the most beautiful blue eyes I had ever seen. This woman who I had decided to hate immediately, was in my hallway, not shaking my hand in an austere, harsh way, but was hugging me and saying how lovely it was to meet me. I don't know about him, but I was in love!

We both stood there, just looking at each other, neither able to stop smiling. She was like a ray of sunshine that had walked into my house and had taken away the clouds. She had also taken me off cold wash and the spin cycle was slowing down. I was stepping out of the washing machine and was being helped out by the one person I was supposed to hate.

"It is so lovely to finally meet you, Emma. I have heard so much about you..."

Oh God, she had heard so much about me from the man who had left, almost done a midnight flit from the biggest loon he had ever met! She would never fall in love with me now. Oh God, I had suddenly developed bisexuality all in the space of a bowl of cereal thrown at me and a doorbell ringing, it was all too much. I think she could see that I was about to have some kind of cadenza so she quickly added,

"From the girls, of course."

Oh thank god, they would have been kind. Jaime can't speak of course so she wouldn't have been able to relay any of the stories of me falling out of my own car or running over her buggy. Abbie would be a slightly different story, she may have to be coached a little, but she will have surely told Chris that I was a kind and funny Mummy with lots of love and laughter and often blowing things up in the kitchen as junior chemistry experiments (how else do you explain daily fires in your oven?) I knew, from that moment, that her and I were going to be friends. The most unlikely of friends, but friends, nonetheless. It was the first time in over a year I felt relief. True relief. A weight had been lifted from these small and accident prone shoulders and it was like being handed a massive medal. You've made it, Emma, you have made it to this point, and it is going to get easier now.

Chapter 6 - Plenty of fish my arse

Ah, brilliant, haven woken up from yesterday's elation that I really like my new replacement with an expression that I have never understood until now, a heavy heart. It literally feels like my heart is going to break through the bottom of my ribcage and leave the building the same way the kids did. Emma, what is wrong with you? She's lovely! She's an ally, she could be a friend? That was it, she was absolutely adorable and so kind and suddenly, it all made sense. I was the problem. Over all those years of my husband finding me physically repulsive for all those months and years of being pregnant and being a wife was actually ALL my fault. This was not part of the emotional recovery plan! This was an unmitigated disaster! Oh God, something had to be done about me and double quick, I could not live with the brand on my head of FAILURE just because the ex had not seen my worth and left me with all the stigmas that go with being a single mother of two tiny children, but also it was ME that was the problem.

Now, if I can explain quickly, I am not a particularly "let's think this through" type of person so internet dating was installed on the ol' PC right there and then my new plan began! This was a win-win situation. I had been alone for over a year and it was time to get the old girl back. AND, it would help me fill those empty evenings when Abbie and Jaime were in bed with something other than a cheap bottle of plonk and *Sleepless in Seattle* – that film always made me feel better as I can't remember the last time I actually slept.

I don't know if this is a normal reaction to internet dating in your 40s but I was deeply ashamed. It was like I had gone out and bought myself a porn hub card or suddenly adopted a gambling addiction. Normally, Izzy would get my call of jubilance that I was back out in that meat market and I was going to meet my Idris Elba. But, no. I even wrote my profile under a slightly disguised name. Of course what I didn't think through (do you see what I mean) was the fact that I used the best photograph of myself I could find to generate some custom so to speak, so what the feckin use the false name was I have absolutely no idea.

Well, the revelation! No more lonely nights in for Miss Insomnia here, I had just got my first poke! You would honestly have thought that the entire cast of *Legends of the Fall* had arrived at my front door and declared undying love for me. I was wanted! Oh yes, this ol' bird has still got it, and then I looked at the profile of the lucky sod who had spotted this "ol' bird" –

"67, but look younger, enjoy long beach walks, movie nights in and support Arsenal and love going to all their games, more of a Monday to Friday guy really. Gained a few pounds over the years so would love the opportunity to lose a few in the sack with you… no time wasters…"

His name was Colin. I am glad to say that I didn't just press delete on the whole website but actually let my mind wander off as to why anyone, who gives birth to a beautiful baby boy then says:

"I know, I am going to call him Colin."

I mean, maybe some avid Colin Firth fans, but still, Colin? For a baby?

Ok, I am losing myself. Colin, is a human being, and I am sure a very nice man so I shall explain, in response to his poke that I am nobody's time waster and I wish him luck. Turns out Colin wasn't a very nice man and said that I bore an uncanny resemblance to Bruce Forsyth in my profile picture. Maybe this wasn't such a good idea after all. But almost as quickly as I was about to press 'abort mission' another 2 pokes.

Well, what could possibly be wrong with these two? There must be some decent men out there, and let's face it, the life I lead the only way I am going to meet one of them is if I push a good one into a supermarket freezer by accident… or one loses control of his car and drives it through my living room wall right at the moment that Tom Hanks finds Meg Ryan at the top of the Empire State Building. No, I shall prevail and I will meet the man of my dreams. Just like Chris had done. And there it was, in all its glory, my motivation. She was going to be SO good for me in SO many ways.

So the days blurred into one another, each starting at about 5am with Jaime teething and Abbie bumbling around knocking things over. By 7am I had normally run out of ideas, so we would turn to our trusty Cbeebies where I had developed some really unhealthy crushes on some of the male presenters (a couple of female ones as well) as I felt they were the only ones who really understood my pain with these small critters that needed constant entertaining, when all I wanted to do was stay in bed and have that well deserved nervous breakdown. We had developed quite a routine which meant that I didn't have to think too much, just work out which day of the week it was and let one mealtime blend into another, attend the various toddler groups with all the happily married mums and talk catalogues with them, whilst having not even enough money to buy the feckin catalogue let alone what was in it and then the dreaded evening witching hours.

These started at about 5pm when you have to think up something imaginative, healthy and palatable for young children. Sounds easy right? Most of them would happily eat a whole tube of after sun and then have their stomachs pumped at A&E for the pleasure. No, it doesn't quite work like that. You think you are going to be one of those Mums who makes fresh, wholesome meals, a different one every night and your little angels will 'wolf it down' – oh how I came to loathe that expression – but of course you never are, well I never was anyway. I discovered 3 meals that they would eat and I stuck to them like glue. I use that expression, because that was the only consistency that Jaime would eat and having had about two mouthfuls of basically pureed spaghetti bolognese she would tip the whole bowl over her head.

Such a funny joke after a long day for about 6 months. I wish I HAD indeed shown more enthusiasm for her little wheeze, because she must have sensed I was getting a tad bored and started throwing the bowl over my head whilst I was wiping up Abbie's mush that she had thrown across the kitchen floor. So, you end up with a kitchen that looks like some kind of explosion happened and you were the main target.

This then leads to bath and bedtime. The joys. You have to join your little gits in the bath to get all the food out of your hair which they think is great fun as with all three of you in there, it is like a feckin swimming pool, and by the time you have finished your part of the pandemonium, so does the bathroom floor. Then it is, what all the perfect Mums call, 'calm time'. It's like one of my kids heard a parent say this at playgroup and thought to herself-

"Not on MY watch!" – this was the 'manic, behave like lunatics from the asylum time' for us. It turns out that they do ingest some of their dinner and it gives them that final burst of energy that you could just feckin do without at this time of night (6pm) which to you feels like you have been clubbing for 12 hours and need to sleep, right now.

Bedtime is always fun too. Two lots of stories, same books every night, same sing song voice with a few tears of exhaustion thrown in and then-

"Night night my gorgeous girls, Mummy loves you, see you in the morning"... Oh how those kids must have laughed when I saw them at least 14 times more until they finally fell asleep and left me to head for my computer to see how many pokes I had got today. It was my only little window of hope that I wasn't going to die alone with liquidised spaghetti all over me and be found by some large yellow labrador cadaver dog only because I tasted so good.

This particular evening was quite productive. One chap looked extremely nice and had not only poked me but had sent me a message too. He sounded NORMAL! Oh my god, I had struck the P of F gold! He told me a little bit about himself, he was a similar age, had 2 children that he spent as much time with as he could, he loved animals and was a keen reader. There had to be a catch, where was the catch? Stop being so cynical, Emma, this could be him, the one!

So I messaged back that it was lovely to hear from him and asked a few questions about where he was based and what his other hobbies were. He replied straight away and it turned out he lived only a matter of a few miles from the madhouse. So, we chatted away and I felt like I was talking to an old friend.

He was a doctor and had worked overseas for many African charities and loved to spend time at the beach. Hmmm, beach, not having much luck being glamorous down there, but I can work on that.

The thing with internet dating is it gives you clarity. The clarity of hindsight is a truly wonderful thing. I chatted away happily to Richard for a few weeks until he finally suggested that we should meet. Oh dear god, really? You want to ruin this marvellously entertaining dalliance with actually seeing me for who I am or vice versa? Why would anyone want to bring reality into this fabulous fantasy? As far as I was concerned, Brad Pitt had stolen himself away from Angelina and was fraternising with a middle aged single mother who had no life and he was going to save her from her Groundhog Day because he loved the Britishness of her stiff upper lip and the fact that she was such an almighty fuck up. And well, Richard was obviously imagining he was picking up the pieces of Jennifer Aniston's car crash of a love life and would be whisking her off to Goring beach in his Fiat 500 (he told me he had a small Italian sports car, I'm a petrol head, it was never going to be a Ferrari). But, ok, it is called Internet 'dating' which I guess means that at some point the chatees have to actually meet and go on a date. Oh god it's all so clinical and horrible. But apparently, much like a pap smear, one has to endure the embarrassment, indignity and pain of the whole palaver in order to achieve the inevitable: good health and eternal happiness. So, we agreed to meet.

The official advice for these events is to meet somewhere public and during the daytime just in case your forever love is in fact a serial killer. At this point in time, I think I would have taken the latter just to put me out of my misery. I spent hours beforehand looking at my profile picture and realising that it was at least 10 years old. I had more hair and my face required far less ironing. It was also taken pre-children and divorce so I actually looked quite happy and relaxed. The truth? I was going to be an enormous let down. I was going to be sued for misleading advertising. So, there I sat, in my hometown's little coffee shop waiting for Brad Pitt in my old jeans and holey jumper. I needed somewhere to put the carnation (his idea). The door opened and thank goodness, a really short slightly dumpy version of my Dad walked in. Must be the new owner's father I thought.

"Emma? Is that you?"

I am not going to lie to you, I did the unthinkable. I looked over my shoulder just to check that there wasn't a slightly more elderly namesake behind me.

To my horror, there was no-one. Just me. Just me and one of my parent's friends. Oh Christ on a bike, what the hell do you do? What the hell do you say? Standing up to greet him was an extremely poor idea as I towered over him like a villainous giant and then shaking him by the hand as he went in for the first peck, actually kissing him on the top of his shining head. Oh for fucks sake I have lost a tooth and left a groaning red incisor mark on the poor man's scalp.

Sit down, Emma, for fucks sake, sit down.

Richard sits down too. He is evidently quite pleased to have finally met me and to realise that my stories of being somewhat accident prone were by no means invented or exaggerated. Oh yes, and I had not in fact lied about my age by approximately an entire generation and had been totally honest about my average height. Now, I am not a judgemental person at all, but really? The poor man had quite obviously just been to get his free bus pass and would without a doubt struggle to get on many of the rides at Thorpe Park – an extremely important part of choosing a future partner. I, on the other hand, although falling apart at the seams emotionally and physically, was only 39 and had thrown up many times on Saw. It was all so confusing. As I sat here, feeling desolate, embarrassed, ashamed and so angry with myself for holding this against this poor man, I was suddenly remembering that I needed to renew Abbie and my annual pass. It was diversion, that was all, diversion.

Ok, task at hand, I need to make this coffee brief, perfunctory and most importantly, I cannot have this man's rejection on my conscience. I refuse to hurt someone else's feelings just because they don't match up to my expectations. I know how horrific that feels. And as if by magic, the door opens and one of my oldest I friends, from primary school drifts in like a southern breeze and she has not changed one bit. Jo, Jo oh my lovely Jo. Born February 13th and signed my end of school autograph book "Keep on skipping - J". I don't think, up until that point anyway, I had ever been so glad to see someone in my life.

"Jo, Jo Clarke?!" I screeched a little too desperately. "Is that really you?"

"Oh wow, Emma, Emma, Emma…" (she had no feckin idea who I was)

"Gardner." someone had to put the poor girl out of hers and my misery.
"Of course, Emma Gardner, wow, long time."

"Yes, unbelievable, what is it? 35 years?"

"Must be, takes me straight back to the days of warm milk in glass bottles and didn't you once throw up in assembly?"

"Yes, yes, that was me. Did I hit you? Apparently quite a few kids got a bit of a splash…" Yes, these words were actually coming out of my mouth much like the vomit that was evidently the only thing that Jo Clarke could remember about me.

"Nah, I just remember the big pile of sand and smell of disinfectant afterwards. That was Miss Burton for you."

"Well, do you fancy joining us? We are just having a quick coffee."

If she didn't recognise the pleading in my eyes from that morning when I begged every child to look down as I left my first assembly at infants school covered in my regurgitated breakfast, then I was doomed. But thank the lord, it was all coming back to her and she saved me with those immortal words,

"Love to, I'll be back in a sec".

I only had the strength to look at my lap for a few moments and then look up at the poor, lovely and totally sweet and elderly doctor in front of me who had possibly been here before, and with my bottom teeth covering my top lip I stared out of the window without the knowledge or the ability to crush this man gently. But, he was a gentleman and I think he realised he had gone a tad too far with the whole age/height thing and that perhaps one day, one of my great aunts may get divorced and I could hook them up, although the whole height thing could be an issue still. But who knows. Richard looked at me apologetically and said,

"I think it's probably best that I go now, you are obviously not attracted to me which I can totally understand, what with you being so young and I had no idea you were so tall.".

"I was sitting down and I haven't been properly measured since I was 14 so I kind of made that part up."

"Richard, I am so sorry, this has been a terrible misunderstanding, I really don't know what to say."

"Don't say anything, Emma, it has been lovely to get to know you. I do find it rather odd that you would lie so much about being older than you are."

For a moment I was both confused and elated. He thinks I am under 30! Yes yes yes! But then I thought, no, I look like utter shit, I haven't slept in about 3 years and I have aged massively since Mike left me. So with no further ado, he left. Before Jo returned, I logged onto my P of F account, and sure enough, there was my age: 59 years old… Oh holy fuck, you utter utter twat Gardner. What in god's name is wrong with you?! Jo returned with her coffee to me with my head in my hands all on my own.

"Got shot of your blind date?" she enquired with a limp smile.

"That obvious?"

"Oh yes, you can see it a mile off. You need some education my lovelie".

Chapter 7 - Will I ever learn?

So here I was. A weird, embarrassing total and utter failure in every sense of the word. I was a rubbish wife, a pretty catastrophic mother and couldn't even work Plenty of feckin Fish properly.
God bless her, Jo took pity on me.

"Look love, fear not, there are plenty of fish left in the sea."

I hoped my withering look was not lost on her.

"Ok, not funny, but true. Look, my boss has just split up from his wife and is gorgeous and single and hasn't got a clue how to meet women. Bit like you really, only a bit less random."

I let that one go.

"If I organise an intro for you both, will you promise me you won't do anything weird or wonderful, he's quite shy and a tad straight if you know what I mean, you might want to ease him into your..."

She's struggling here.

"The - I need cones around me, personality. Just be you, but with some of the 'you' taken out, just for a while..."

Oh to hell with it, in for a penny. I can do normal for an evening.

"Do your worst Jo! He sounds gorgeous and I promise to be on my best behaviour."

"He might not go for it, but I swear I will do my best and do the best sales job for you."

Was that bit really necessary? She sees my face.

"I won't mention the whole getting in the wrong car and finding your car keys in the freezer for example, ooooooh and I won't bring up you getting decked by that belly dancer in London when you tried to take over her show when we were at Collyers. Wow, she really knew how to throw a punch! Remember?"

"Yes, yes, I remember. I ended up in some poor divorcee's souffle, he cried too."

"Oh my God, yes! I won't mention that."

We say our goodbyes and I am less than hopeful that anything will come from this new potential liaison.

As I put Jaime and Abbie to bed that night, I found myself feeling strangely wistful. There was a strange calm about me, about them too. I read them both a story, and for the first time in what seemed ages, it was not through gritted teeth or with a slight sob in my voice, I actually made it funny and before I knew it, we were all hysterical with laughter. Jaime even fell off the bed. Something she would go onto to do with alarming regularity. But for tonight, something had shifted. Had I shed some despair? Or was it hope? I know there was the most extraordinary amount of love in that moment and I wanted to hang onto it forever. That moment and moments like it would be my oxygen. So I read another story, and we laughed some more and the colours became more oranges and purples and when I woke up, we were all in my bed, girls were fast asleep and the feeling was still there. I was guessing. I knew it. But in a brief moment, I knew, somehow, that everything was going to be alright.

Morning came soon enough. 5am is always too early, no matter who you are or how you are feeling. Jaime had gone downstairs and tipped milk all over her head and was busy pouring frosties on the floor so she could have a 'picnic breakfast' – ok, so this whole being alright in the end thing might take some time. I headed for the washing machine, full of feckin water.

Oh what now?! Opened the filter and 3 swimming pool's worth of frogs spawn spewed out all over the kitchen lino. What the actual fuck is this. We were wading through it and I was the only one who was apparently horrified. Abbie and Jaime thought this was absolutely fabulous.

I started rummaging around in the washing machine to see what on earth could have caused us to be knee deep in water full of plastic bubbles. Nothing. I look at the two little gits who were having their own little water party.

"Abbie? Jaime? Did anyone put anything in the washing machine yesterday?"

Abbie is beaming from ear to ear.

"Jaime was a good girl, she did a poo nappy and put it in there so you wouldn't have to clean it up..."

Little gag. Then slightly larger gag when I realised that we were all paddling around in some kind of shit covered silicone. Amazing the strength you have when you need to pick up two small people at the same time. One under each arm, straight into the bath upstairs. They're all dry. Now to tackle the kitchen floor. Buckets just aren't fucking big enough and this was a monumental task. When I had managed to clear up a vast majority of the shit flood, I then realised I had to move the washing machine which, as it turns out, was hiding the other 50% of the crap behind it. So in one swift movement, I not only made a mansize tear in the lino I released the rest of the shit grenade from behind the hotpoint.

Defeated. Feckin defeated. The tears come far too easily. There I am, covered in faeces, water and some really weird smelling chemicals with a bloody great hole in the kitchen floor and another half a swimming pool to bail out when the phone rings.
Oh please be Mike, please please please be Mike, I am SO ready for a scrap and to actually tell him, in no uncertain terms what he has done to me and my life. But no. It is a stranger's voice.

"Hi, is that Emma?"

"Uh yes, yes, it is. Who is this?"

"It's Steve, Steve Jones, Jo's boss... are you ok?"

Turns out it's quite difficult to muffle the noises of attempting to get up from a floor that is soaked, as are you, with a snotty nose from crying and there is still some minor gagging going on.

"Oh yeah, I am just great. I am sitting here, in a pool of..." just about to say liquid poo but remembered to take some of the "me" out of me.

"Milk that one of the kids spilt. Kids heh?"

"Yeah, I've got a couple myself. Look, let's not make this awkward, Jo said you were a lovely, albeit a slightly weird girl and that you would be up for going out for a drink sometime?"

"Uh yes, that would be lovely. Did you have any particular time in mind?"

"Well, I am free this evening if you are...."

Oh dear god, this is going to involve Emma's army. Mum, Dad, Izzy and possibly a few plumbers, not to mention my lovely hairdresser Adam. But I can do this. If Mike can win himself a beauty and live the dream, then so can I!

"You're on Steve. Are you sure you're ready for me?" – meant to be playful, actually I could hear tangible fear.

"I think so, Jo has mentioned that weird shit happens to you. Any chance of keeping some of that on its leash tonight? I have a big meeting tomorrow."

"Sure, sure thing."

Oh Emma, don't try to be cool.

"I actually CAN be normal you know, well sometimes anyway."

You could feel the back peddling on the other end of the line. So Emma's dedicated and totally loyal army sprung into action and by 7pm there was only a slight smell of shit in the house and I was coiffured and actually had put makeup on BOTH eyes. Not looking too ropey even if I say so myself.

As the hour of 8pm approached, the nerves started to get the better of me. Oh God, what have I done? I am not normal, I am a total human fuck up. He is going to see this immediately and run for the hills. But, too bloody late now. Just keep spraying the house with air freshener, all the windows are open, distract yourself.

There it is. The ring of the doorbell. Last little look in the mirror and a little sexy shake of the head and the door gets opened. Holy mother of god, he is HOT! Tall, handsome, beautiful warm smile. Oh, a little in love. The most dangerous part of this whole moment is I am instantly relaxed and have completely forgotten not to be me. Well here goes...

Chapter 8 - THE blind date to end all blind dates

We go to a gorgeous little pub where no-one knows me (bonus one) and we have a really lovely dinner which I managed not to wear any of (bonus two). The conversation is flowing, he's so gorgeous and sweet, a little bit funny and SO interesting and even better, interested (bonus three). The cynic in me says this is WAY too good to be true. As an eternal optimist, there are two things that I fail to do.

1. Fail to listen to the cynic in me

2. Remember, in situations like this, the cynic is ALWAYS right

But, a couple of lovely glasses of cold white Sauvignon Blanc and this beautiful man in front of me has removed me from my world of chaos and mayhem and I am just loving being the old me. The one who can engage people without wearing either her own food or her children's and there is nothing, bloody nothing I can set fire to here. It's only bloody Emma proof!!!

We get to my front door and with a child-free house and the evening having gone so well, I do the unthinkable. I invited him in. No no no, I don't do the whole, 'fancy a coffee?', 'I don't drink coffee.' 'Don't worry I haven't got any coffee' thing. This man is much more reserved for that, this is just to get to know each other a little better. I am truly surprised when he says yes! He came in and sat on my sofa. To my relief the gentle smell of Jaime's poo nappy incident had left the building. Time to close all the windows as it was bloody freezing and I lived in hope that the neighbour's cat hadn't snuck in, which it sometimes did, and often would fly out at me like a fucking ninja and scare the shit out of me. Now that WOULD ruin this lovely evening.

Within a matter of minutes I noticed that the lovely, gorgeous, totally hot Steve (careful Emma, back things up a little) seemed to be in a little facial discomfort. His eyes were a little red and he was starting to get a tad blotchy.

"Are you ok?" I asked tentatively.

Please please don't let him be allergic to children's poo. Some of it must still be around somewhere. To my relief, he asked me if I had a cat.

"Horribly allergic to cat fur you see."

"No, no, we don't have one... although the neighbour's cat sometimes pays us a visit, a bit like *The Pink Panther's* manservant Cato. She jumps out and attacks me randomly and we have to wrestle with each other to see who wins... (I see fear now)... it doesn't happen very often though, so I am sure you'll be fine."

Diversion. Coffee. I sit on the floor next to him. Slightly tarty move, but am feeling a little risqué and very much Carpe that fucking Diem (more like Drink-e that fucking Vino).

The conversation suddenly seems to dry up. Steve is evidently still struggling with his allergy as he is rubbing his eyes an awful lot but I am not to be deterred, and so as I am unable to deal with awkward silences, I begin telling him about watching a show with Frank Skinner as the presenter. He had been attending a tantric sex farm which I had found highly amusing. Steve seemed a little confused as to what tantric sex was so I took the opportunity of educating him having watched keenly as Frank Skinner not only made it funny but hugely informative too.

Huge note to self, Emma: you are not Frank Skinner, you are you and this was never going to go well.
I start going into great detail trying to explain what I understood it to be; lots of suggestion, erotic non-touching sexually and basically not actually doing anything really other than the odd bit of finger sucking etc.

Suddenly, assuming he had got the general idea, he presented me with his index finger pointing upwards. Old feckin looney tunes here thinks blimey he's up for a bit of this, so with no further ado or hesitation, I throw caution to the wind and pop his finger in my mouth and began (in the most seductive way I could muster) a little bit of gentle sucking (oh who the fuck am I kidding, I was like a lamb to a bottle!).

Expecting a little more enthusiasm from his side, I was a little taken aback when he looked at me in horror and said-

"Jesus Emma, WHAT THE FUCK ARE YOU DOING?"

Sadly, I was not taken aback quite enough to actually have removed his finger from my mouth and so mumbled back with my mouth well and truly full,

 "Ummm, I'm sucking your finger..."

Hoping this would clear the whole situation up I slowly and very gingerly removed his finger and tried to establish some decorum to the atmosphere.

The silence is agony. He looks positively panic stricken and genuinely upset.

"Oh God, Steve, have I done something wrong?" he is starting to get seriously agitated now. Has he had a terrible experience with finger sucking in his past?! Did a former girlfriend leave him for Frank Skinner?

Good god, what on earth have I done?!

His response is something I will never, for the rest of my life forget:

"Emma... You-have-just-eaten-my-bloody-contact-lens..."

It was said very slowly, very definitely, so there could be NO doubt that he was heard clearly. I now know why dogs put their heads on one side when they are not sure what you have just said to them.
Ok, it is starting to sink in now. Oh Christ on a bike. Emma. Emma. Emma.

The gagging started.

He had removed his contact lens accidentally, and then I had done what any normal, totally feckin unhinged human being would do, I ate the fucking thing thanks to Frank Skinner and his bloody tantric sex farm. I have NEVER in my life seen someone exit my house so quickly. He actually tripped a couple of times but raced out he did, I saw the whites of the poor man's eyes – well ok, only the one.

He was gone. All sense of hope and dignity had gone with him. I can't be sure how long I sat on the floor with my head in my hands for, but it took a whole lot of breathing in and out to be able to look up and face the fact that what had happened was not a nightmare, it was just me being me. Sleep did not come easily and when it did, it did not last long. I had to face the music the following morning. I rang Jo:

"Hi love, how are you?"

The sing-song voice was a total give away.

"How's Steve?" I continued.

"Emma, what the actual fuck! You ate his contact lens?! How in God's bloody name did you manage that?!"

"It was a misunderstanding, an accident, I thought he wanted me to..."

"You thought he wanted you to eat his contact lens? Really Emma? I told you not to be you. The poor man looked positively terrified when he came in this morning and told me he had to drive home with one hand over one eye or he would've crashed!"

"Oh bugger, Jo, I am so sorry. You're not in trouble are you?"

"No, no, nothing like that. He just asked me to be more specific about what 'weird stuff' means when I set him up again."

"So I guess he doesn't want to see me again then..."

"I don't think he will be able to love... "

Her hysteria is totally understandable but I am still struggling to see the funny side of my ridiculousness ruining, what could have potentially be a grand new start, and now I have nothing to show for all the efforts that went into that perfect date; except a contact lens making its way through my small intestines as we speak.

"Ok, say sorry to him for me. I hope they weren't expensive, I'm happy to let him know when I pass it and pop it into some steriliser."

Jo suddenly had a conference call then and off she popped.

Chapter 9 - The politics of primary school

Another day, another contact lens. When you are a parent, single or otherwise, you have to accept that every day is a case of forgetting what went before and keep dusting yourself off and carrying on. There is no 'giving up' or wallowing in self pity time. It's full steam ahead and the kids don't give a flying monkeys if you ate someone's visual aid the night before and shattered all your dreams in the process. They still want feeding 3 times a day and being entertained for 15 hours.

So, the days blurred into weeks, and the weeks into months and life carried on. Now that Chris and I had realised that we were allies rather than enemies, the weekend visits up to their father's were so much easier. We met halfway, everything felt more normal and I felt so much happier knowing that they were safe and well looked after by this goddess. I swear to god she got prettier every time I saw her. The girls always came back relentlessly talking about how amazing her cooking was and how they loved her dog. They were happy and that made me happy. I had dreaded how this whole co-parenting thing was going to work, but with the addition of Chris, it had all started to work amazingly well. I wanted to hate her. She had what I had wanted.

But she was a Godsend and dealing with her over the arrangements with the kids was infinitely easier than dealing with Mike. The whole arrangement seemed to be suiting him too. Peace was here at last. There was I again, ignoring the cynic in me. But when you are always awaiting the start of the washing machine, you have to take the good times and wrap them up. Because as my mother always told me, nothing ever stays the same, both good and bad. Her version of 'this too shall pass'. And how right she was.

The girls started at the village school. The perfect start for any young child. So small, so personal, such a gentle introduction to an institution that would form the next 12 years of their daily lives. They took to it like fish to water. I wasn't quite as smooth as they were. It was here, the school playground, that I came across competitive women at their finest and having 'Single Mother' stamped on your forehead meant that trying to keep up with these extraordinary machines was absolutely fucking pointless.

Yes, I found my new niche. The Village School Idiot and I was damned good at it.

Permission slips became my new nemesis. I cannot even begin to count the occasions that my poor kids nearly missed trips of a lifetime because their twat of a mother forgot to fill in a permission slip. I got so despondent about getting a royal bollocking from the school secretary that I decided to go in with a solution for my complete lack of competence with primary school paperwork (this should be a feckin job description for a University graduate).

"Hi Mrs S, me again."

"Ah Mrs Gardner, do you have a permission slip for me, or have you actually managed to find Jaime's story sack from two years ago?"

The last 3 words were spat at me.

"Uh no, and sort of."

"I have no idea what that means Mrs Gardner, but I am sure you are about to explain."

That woman really should get her facial expressions under control.

"Ok, look, I know I am absolutely shit at remembering anything…"

"Can I stop you there Mrs Gardner, these walls are thin and there are impressionable young people here, could you please watch your language…"

Oh God, she wasn't going to like the next bit.

"Ok, sorry, so look, I seem to be plagued with an illness. I was diagnosed a few years ago and that means that my memory is not what it should be, hence all the forgotten permission slips and always being late for really important meetings etc. So, I have an idea. Perhaps for the foreseeable, I could give you a kind of blanket permission slip which basically gives you my written permission to take my kids anywhere, apart from out of the country or the middle east or whatever, what do you think?"

"Oh Mrs Gardner, I am so sorry, I feel awful, I had no idea."

Ah shit. She's feeling sorry for me. I am about to either get lambasted or we are going to find some common ground here. It's a gamble. I'm going to take it.

"If I may ask, what is this illness?"

Here we go.

"Well, it's called CRAFT disease. It's not very well known but strangely common in women like myself."

"Gosh, I have never heard of that. What does CRAFT stand for?"

Deep breath, Emma, Deep breath. Just say it really quickly-

"Can't Remember A Fucking Thing".

Our eyes meet.
She's making a decision.
It is definitely about me living or dying.

I can almost hear the mud behind her ears starting to crack. She is definitely going to smile, she's smiling! I have triumphed!!! Finally, I am no longer a pariah. Go me! So, I have won over the school secretary, now to win over the extremely austere Headmistress and to win the respect of my peers in the playground.

Tough crowd. Didn't go well.

I started by suggesting to the Head that a wonderful way to make great hoards of cash for the school would be to shake a bucket at the largest gathering of the village parents ever known to man (the local pub on a Friday). The sky darkened, a large crack of lightning from above (ok, so I made that bit up, but fuck me it was scary) She pulled down her spectacles and like a scarier version of Nanny McPhee she cast a dark shadow over me and said,

"We are a Church of England school, Ms Gardner, and couldn't possibly be associated with money raised in a "public house where money is made from the sale of alcohol." (She actually growled the word alcohol). I was not aware that the whole bloody playground had been listening whilst gossiping, but the HUSH that fell over that whole load of feckin perfect parents was bloody deafening. Oh FFS. It's always me. I am the fall guy, the scapegoat, and in this case, the bloody mouthpiece because actually, this was NOT my idea AT ALL – I just wanted to go to the pub after school on Friday and get battered.

Someone else's bright idea to rob the pub of its small change. That's not the point. Once again, I was cringing and desperately trying to find that ever elusive 'evaporation button'. Blood red with embarrassment and most of the mothers giggling away at my seemingly relentless ability to be the school playground twat, they all backed off so as not to be associated with the village idiot.

Apart from that one loyal friend. That one, bloody bastard loyal friend whose bastard idea it was. She had the vague decency to stand stock still and see how the fuck I was going to get out of this one. Then I had an epiphany. This is rarely a good thing. This was no exception. This fell out of my mouth, and for some reason I suddenly had a broad Yorkshire accent (bastard friend is from Yorkshire).

"Didn't Jesus once turn water into't wine? At some point... at some gathering, not a pub or anything.. just sayin'..."

The pause indicates the density of the glare that I got. The hush amongst the perfect parents was so loud that I knew several of them had actually stopped breathing.

"Can I see you in my office, Ms Gardner?"

Oh shit feck twatty bollocks. 43 year old in detention. Fucking marvellous. So epic and pretty permanent fail with the Headmistress and slightly on the back foot with the 'Perfect Parent brigade'– but that is not a done deal, I CAN and WILL overcome that little stumbling block.

I didn't do anything radical like join the PTA, I knew that would have my cover blown in a matter of minutes, but I did take part in any volunteering to help out with school fairs and such like. That's easy, you set fire to the odd sausage on the barbecue at the fete and don't get asked again.

The school also had a great idea to raise money by raffling a homemade cake every Friday. One particular Friday afternoon at pick up one of the lovely little girls, who was great friends with my youngest daughter, filed out of school at the end of a Friday with her bottom lip quivering and tears welling in her eyes. I was standing with her mother who was desperately worried as to what was wrong with little Claire.

"Sweetheart, what on earth is the matter?" asked her mum.

"I won the cake raffle, Mummy."

"But that's lovely darling, we can have some for tea."

"Someone's Mum forgot to make a cake, Mummy."

And with that the flood gates opened and this distraught little thing crumbled. She had never won the cake raffle before and this was a huge accolade. Gasps of horror all around.

So gob on a stick here, reaches out to her emotional Mum and says really loudly:

"Oh please don't worry sweetheart, I am sure the Mummy will make it up to you and anyway, I can take you to the shop and get an ice cream, and you can stroke Spencer."

I look at her mother and say in a really loud voice-

"Oh God, how bloody awful, that's the kind of thing I would do!"

With that out comes my 7 year old:

"IT *WAS* YOU, MUMMY!"

They just walk away shaking their heads.

Chapter 10 - The return of reality

Walking home with two disappointed and dejected children. Hardly surprising, they have a total buffoon for a mother who has just had to ask for credit in the village sweet shop because she has forgotten her purse. The fact that I congratulated myself for not actually shoplifting the sweets and then asking the children if I had just said that out loud did not go down well either. It's starting to rain. Can today get any worse? This is a question that I often ask the universe without wanting it to be an actual request. But so often it is not only society as a whole that misunderstands me, but the universe as well. I walked in and the phone was ringing. Today was going to get a whole lot worse.

It was Chris. Beautiful, perfect and happy Chris. The one with my other life. But she is crying. She is crying a lot.

"Chrissie, sweetheart, what on earth is the matter?"

Thoughts fly through my head. Her mother has died, her dog has been hit by a car, her cancer is back. The terrible possibilities are endless and I suddenly feel absolute desperation and compassion for my replacement.

"Can I talk to you, Emma, like really talk to you, in confidence?"

Can she? I don't know. I really hardly know this person but every instinct I have as a woman and a mother says that there is no way I can turn this girl away. She has reached out to the most unlikely confidant so it must be serious.

"Of course you can love, what's happened?"

"We're breaking up."

I haven't heard this right. I have stopped breathing for a few seconds. It feels like my blood has changed temperature by about 3 degrees. I have gone cold. It's happening again. He's leaving.

Just as fast I snap back into Chris's reality, not my own.

"What? What the fuck? Oh Jesus, Chris, you have got to be kidding me?"

I now realise that my heart is racing and not in a good way. In the past few years, when Mike and I have had civilised conversations about the wellbeing of the kids, he has never actually apologised for, or even explained his totally unforeseen and untimely departure from the girls' and my life - but he has told me how Chris is the love of his life and he would die for her. I was sure he once tried to produce tears when he broke the news to me that she had had a cancer diagnosis, but didn't quite manage actual moisture, but said that his world had come apart. I remember thinking, at the time, that if I loved someone that much my life too would come apart, but perhaps that would not be my first focus. But then, there was the cynic in me about my ex husband. I am convinced he is actually a nice guy, despite what he did to us and with no apparent remorse. He MUST be a great guy. Chris would never fall in love with a cretin. My children could not have a snake for a father. The breakdown of our marriage was because I lost my figure and my entire personality whilst I was pregnant and then basically turned into a living breathing cow whilst the kids were small and I was trying and failing to breastfeed. That was my doing. He was not to blame for my inadequacies.

But now I am faced with some new realities. She is holding on to the other end of the phone sobbing.

"Ok, love, one step at a time. Slowly talk me through what has happened. I am sure there must be a mistake?"

So, she did, and it became apparent that there was no mistake. Mike and her were splitting up. My heart broke for her. She had come to live in England to be with Mike after they had met again after knowing one another many years earlier. She had given up her business, her family, her home and all for this moment of pure heartache. I have managed to stop her crying a bit. She is calm.

"Listen love, life isn't perfect, good God, I am living proof of that! But, nothing is impossible. You two can get over this. You two are made for each other, he adores you."

"Oh I don't know about that, he hasn't been exactly the model boyfriend and he is under no illusion that all his stuff will be on the pavement when gets back... and when I say all his stuff, his clothes and his toothbrush! That is all I found him with 6 years ago. He said you took everything... Good for you by the way!"

Long. Hard. Pause.

"Chrissie, can you say that again for me, love?"

"Which bit?"

"The bit about how long ago you found him?"

"6 years ago... well 6 years and 2 months almost to the day..."

"We were still married then. Jaime was 2 months old. He went away on business to Europe and..."

Oh shit fuck. Oh seriously, shit fuck bollocks.

"Emma, what are you talking about? You and Mike had been divorced for 6 months when I met him?"

"Um, no, we had just had Jaime. I thought that we would be fine and he promised me that I was still the woman of his world, the mother of his children and we would get through this tough time... I even threw him a big surprise birthday party a few months before he left..."

"Oh dear God" she said.

"That was the flight that he missed..."

I think at this point we were both sitting down on the floor. Without even realising it, I had tears pouring down my face. How did I know? My youngest daughter was wiping them away with some loo roll.

"You ok, Mummy?"

"Yes-yes sweetheart, Mummy is fine. Just sad news. Go and grab yourself a brioche (the solver of all solvers in our house)

"Oh Chris, I don't know what to say. I fear we have both been duped."

Then it all started coming out. I had to know everything. She had to know everything. What I was about to embark on, with Chris, was a journey with 'shock' in the driver's seat. Shock took us on a voyage of about 4 different emotions a minute. It steered us into places we thought we would never go and it showed us the darkest corners of two broken hearts. It was a journey that was only just beginning and it was one that we were not able to disembark.

The coming days were tough. I had to continue being Mummy to two little tikes, dealing with tantrums, fights, food being tipped over each others' heads, permission slips both remembered and forgotten and the joys of bath and bedtime with the turbulence that was my daughter's' lovely stepmother's world unravelling and her tangible pain It should not have been my roller-coaster, but I was on it nonetheless and I was not in a position to get off. I was so fond of her and it was like reliving my own pain of rejection. I was also sworn to secrecy by Chris. She was still in a state of disbelief and heartbreak and was still not entirely sure what her next move should be.

The children's visits to their father were put on hold for a while as the atmosphere up North was somewhat arctic, although Chris was desperate to see the girls. Not having any biological children of her own, she had quickly fallen for my two little buggers. They adored Chris. Slowly but surely things started to settle down and although Chris and I talked on a daily basis about how devastated she felt, I talked her into staying put for a while as everyone makes mistakes and I assured her that Mike had never looked at me the way he looks at her and in all his and my communication, she had always been at the centre of his world.

She seemed more convinced. Time passed, the children's visits resumed and life went back to some sort of settled normality. The colours of our lives had reverted back from a dark dark blue to something resembling the purple and orange that we loved so much. But the shade and brightness was somewhat dimmed.

Chapter 11 - Fate and Destiny

I was woken one morning in August to a phone call. One of my oldest friends from school.

"Morning love, I will be with you at about 2ish, is that ok?"

Shit fuck bollocks, what on earth was Sarah doing coming down today and why the feck do I know nothing about it?!

"Perfect sweetheart, remind me again, what are we doing?"

"Oh Emma, you are feckin hopeless! It's Lottie's college reunion, everyone will be there, we've been planning this for months!"

"Oh yes, of course, so we have."

My heart is suddenly in my boots. I am broke, I haven't had a haircut for about a year, my face shows the amount of years I haven't slept for, but the fact that I look like Mrs Doubtfire is the least of my problems. This group of people are the high achievers. They all ended up at Uni and no doubt have either high flying jobs or are married to hugely successful men who all have said high flying jobs, they probably have personal shoppers for fuck's sake! I treat a trip to the supermarket as a 'mini-break'. And here I am, a bedraggled, knackered single mother with two, working 4 days a week at a pub and barely clinging onto that job because I am so shit at it. This week I have dropped a total of 5 bottles of spirits and smashed at least 15 glasses. I am on my last warning. I am 42 and I am just about to be fired from a pub job for being utterly shit at that!

"You know what Sarah, love, you are more than welcome to stay here but I have got no childcare, no money and... Oh fuck it, I would rather stick hot needles in my eyes before going to this party!"

Tears were stinging at my eyes at this point. Because I meant it. The old Emma would have bloody loved a do like this. It would have been the perfect chance to catch up with some really old friends who have not seen each other for years and laugh at how old we all are now and how we had fucked up our lives royally.

Rather more different when you actually have fucked up your life royally and feel totally worthless as a result. I knew it was more of a case of not actually being able to face these people rather than just not particularly wanting to. I couldn't do it. Mike and the past 6 years had removed whatever bit of my personality made me capable of being ok. I was not ok. I was broken. It suddenly dawned on me that I had only just realised that and there was no way in hell they were going to be the first people that would see it. Broken Emma. Unfixable Emma. Flattened and defeated Emma.

Long silence from Sarah.

"Honestly love, I feel the same. I am dreading it, but you know what, these are the things you HAVE to go to to prove to yourself that you can."

"But, I actually can't love. I picture myself walking into that marquee, seeing all those faces who I loved so much 25 years ago and I know I will either throw up on the spot or burst into tears and run away. Not really the ideal way to reintroduce yourself to 'the gang' is it?"

"You'll be fine. You're just scared. I'm scared. We can do this."

"No, you don't understand. I am not me anymore. Well, what I mean is, I am not her anymore. She's gone. She's been replaced with a single mother with PTSD and NO plan to improve. In fact, I have realised in the past few minutes, my plan is to deteriorate until the kids are old enough for me to have the nervous breakdown I am due. All those other girls will be planning their enormous wedding anniversary parties or talking about their upcoming holiday home that they're buying. I will be saving up for my straight jacket and prolonged stay in a mental institution."

"I love it, you see, you can still make me laugh. Nothing has really changed, you are still you, just a bit battered around the edges, but that just makes you funnier..."

I realised at that point that Sarah was never going to understand that that statement I had just made was not only no joke, but I had only just realised the gravity of it myself. I was a monumental fuck up. My only ambition was to make it through my children's childhoods and then head to the nearest mental facility to be put back together.

There it was, my future and she wanted me to not only face this for the first time but to have a great big long hard look at my heavenly past and the promise it showed, all on the same day.

Not gonna happen.

"Nope, sorry love. I can't do it. Tell them I have the norovirus. It's not hard to believe as we get it as a family at least every 3 months, I am due for a dose."

"Emma, no, please please come. I can't do this on my own. I feel the same. Unmarried, no kids, got a good career, but I have failed in so many ways. My plan didn't pan out either. They won't judge, they're not like that. Please come."

They won't judge. Do I care about THEM? Do I care if they judge my total lack of life, the fact that my dreams have been shattered and that I am living a parallel life to the one I wanted? No, it wasn't them. It was me. I couldn't bear seeing my own disappointment in myself, reflected in their eyes and remembering who I used to be. Being taken back to fun loving, couldn't give a damn about anything, Emma, was just going to be too painful. Right at that moment I realised what Mike had taken from me.

He had taken ME.

Apparently, I was not going to get away with this easily. Sarah was determined to get me to this freaking party so she commandeered 'She That Must Be Obeyed' - aka my mother!

"Emma, pull your head out of your backside, bring my granddaughters over here and get yourself to that reunion. You only have to stay for an hour or so, have a couple of lemonades and then come home."

Yep, great Mum, an hour is more than long enough to bring forward the nervous breakdown by about 2 years. But, hey, she was in charge and she also held the key to the cupboard with the babysitting tokens in so torture it was. Sarah arrived and the bitch looked bloody amazing. Hadn't aged a bit and didn't just have a good career, had a feckin incredible one! Frontline War journalist. So similar to barmaid at the local it was unreal.

She made me change out of my filthy jeans and poured me into a dress that I hadn't worn for 15 years and brushed my hair.

"There, you look a picture!"

I looked like a picture of Pat Butcher.

Every part of my anatomy, two in particular, were determined to leave the dress and how many rolls of fat can one woman have?! They could have just added nipples to them all and I could have least said that I had just stopped breastfeeding puppies! But hey ho, off we jolly well go.
I am numb now. I have found that switch in my head that I use every time I have to see Mike take my girls from me for their monthly over nighter. My auto pilot button. Not ideal when you want to shine and radiate middle aged success, but a jolly effective coping mechanism nonetheless and I was going to need every single one of those today. We walked into the most beautiful garden I had ever seen. There they all were. The Gang. Still the same, still all gorgeous and fun and interestingly, not all so successful and glowingly happy after all. It was after about 10 minutes I started to relax and Sarah asked if it was ok to let go of my hand now and went on to explain that I was a bit nervous rather than the fact that we were now an item. Although that did then lead on to our mutually disastrous love lives.

I tried to keep my explanation as brief as possible so as not to focus on it, but the more I had to repeat it in its shortest form:

"Got married, had two kids, husband left after the second one was born."
End of.

It got me thinking that that really was what actually happened. There were no frilly, dramatic bits. He arrived, we married, we had two kids and he then left. I had never really thought in too much detail about this. I was just discarded. I was a broodmare, chosen for my pedigree, bred from and then, yes, just discarded, like old rubbish. Put out grass. Extraordinarily simple really. In all fairness, I did have a look of an old horse – long face, largeish nose and a good ol' pair of gnashers...

The party progressed quite well, and I felt there were bits of the old Emma that were not only emerging but were almost unharmed. I still had a sharp sense of the ridiculous about me, which over the past few years, I thought was actually me believing and hating the fact that I was ridiculous, but it was starting to feel like being totally ridiculous was actually pretty fucking ok. It certainly made some of my old mates laugh and as the afternoon wore on, I started to wear ridiculous quite well, I thought it rather suited me. I might keep this new outfit, this ridiculousness. It fitted and I felt comfortable. My new found revelation that being a ridiculous twat was something to be celebrated was rudely interrupted by one of my favourite people from school, who I hadn't seen or heard of for 25 long years, who crept up behind me and put his hands over my eyes.

"Oi Calamity, how the devil are you?"

Eddie, my lovely friend Eddie.

I spun around and took a rather sharp intake of breath. I had never fancied Eddie at college. He was a classic 80's wally with peroxide blonde HUGE hair and a daft grin on his face. He was most definitely one of my favourite people in the world back then, mainly because of his eternal kindness and he had one of those smiles that reached every part of his face. He was geeky but adorable.

Now he was just adorable. Where did that hairy chest come from and jeez, he'd really toned up and grown into that smile.

Oh no, please Emma, no. Men are not part of your ridiculous plan. They complicate everything and no-one will buy into a future of work, raise children, drink wine, work, raise children, drink wine and save for a nervous breakdown. No, this was not going to be part of any plan. Anyway, Eddie was Eddie, and he would be married and have hundreds of kids and a fabulous job so put all that out of your mind. NOW.

"Eddie! Oh my God, Edster! How are you ol' git?"

"I am good Calamity, you look amazing, how are you?!"

Two choices. Right now. Stock response, the big lie or the truth?

This is Ed. We are alone, no-one can hear us. Fuck it, be brave Emma Dilemma. Do it.

"Eddie, I am utterly shit. I am a total fuck up. I fall over a lot, I have two beautiful children who think I am totally bonkers and I work in a pub. I get in the wrong car at petrol stations in my pyjamas and I clean up a lot of spilled drinks and vomit. I fucked it all up, Eddie, I got it all wrong."

I drew breath. Too much? I looked up to see whether he was actually still there as I realised that I had done my monologue whilst staring at my feet so as not to see the look of pity on his face. He would have expected more of me. I had the upper hand back then, when Emma was brave and not broken. He was still there. There was no pity. He just smiled that extraordinary smile and pulled me into him, threw those beautiful arms around me and whispered in my ear,

"Me too, kiddo, me too."

The rest of the party was a bit of a blur after that. It turns out that Eddie had filed for divorce the day beforehand after a very abusive marriage and was riding the wave of shame with me. He also nearly didn't come but was bullied relentlessly by HIS mother to not be so pathetic and get his arse down to see all his old friends.

The afternoon turned into the evening and I had totally lost track of time. It had literally been years since I had lost track of time. My life was totally controlled by routine, meals, school runs and bedtimes. When was the last time that I had no idea what the time was. But time suddenly did catch up with me and I had to go and collect the girls from my Mum. My bubble was about to burst and I was about to say goodbye to my Ed for another 25 years no doubt.

I stood looking at him for a moment, breathing in the way he made me feel like I was 16 again and the world was at my feet. I didn't want to let that go. I didn't want to let go of the old Emma Dilemma. And just like that, he made it so I didn't. He asked me if he could have my number and we could meet up. Talk divorce and all that jazz.

Those were his words. Not the ideal chat-up line, but I wasn't even thinking about ideals, I was thinking about hope. For the first time in a long time, I felt this overwhelming feeling that had been so absent from my psyche for what felt like forever, a sense of hope.

Sarah and I said our farewells and I glanced over my shoulder and caught Eddie smiling at me with a look of mutual recognition. He too, at that moment, felt hope.

Chapter 12 - Always be late

The week had started badly. That norovirus that I tempted with my attempted lie hit us all again like a bloody hurricane. These sick bugs are seriously efficient. They rarely strike you all on the one night so you can just sit in the bath and vomit together, get no sleep and cry a lot and then all have a duvet day with lucozade and marmite toast the next day with movies and napping.

Oh no, they get one of you, normally I go first. Spent the entire night with my head over the loo trying to fondly remember nights like that that were self inflicted and I had actually enjoyed the evening up until that point. You are then awoken from your new found sleeping spot by daughter number 1 who wants to know why you are asleep on the bathroom floor and why everything smells sick? Oh, and look, goodie, it is 5.30am, I must have grabbed at least 20 minutes. The day begins. Under these conditions, it is the unspoken law that you do not call for armed backup. Oh no, you are now under house arrest and need to put a bloody great cross on the door and wait for the cart to come past calling:

"Bring out your dead". So, this is it, you are on your lonesome.

I battled my way through the day somehow. My heroes being CBeebies and Pixar and bathed the kids and put them to bed and collapsed in my own bed at 6.30pm.

I am dying, it is official.

The phone rings, oh do fuck off. Whoever you are, I am not to be messed with this evening. But I always have this ominous feeling that if I don't answer I will regret it somehow.

"Hello..."

"Em, hi, is that you?"

"I think so. Hard to tell. Who is this?"

"Oh God, sorry, it's Eddie. Have I caught you at a bad time?"

Oh god, am I going to be sick again? Or are those butterflies? It's been so long.

"Hey Ed, no, this is a great time. Last night would have been tricky unless you were one of the people that used to hold my hair back at those magnificent parties at college, in which case it would have been a trip down memory lane..."

Too much information.

"We've been hit with the dreaded sick bug, sorry, you didn't need to know that."

"Oh God, poor you. Have you got any help?"

"No, just me. It's ok, hopefully it will end with me. Most things do."

Totally self piteous and attention seeking. Come on Emma, this is your moment, you may reek of puke and have about as much life in you as a wet match, but don't blow this.

"Well, I was wondering if you were around at all this weekend? I don't have my kids and I was thinking of heading down to the coast on my new motorbike. You said you love the beach, I thought you might like a visitor?"

Oh my God oh my God oh my God, this is a date. He's asking me out on a date!

"Not a date or anything, just old mates getting together talking divorce."

So not a date then.

"Eddie, sure, sounds great. The forecast is good and assuming that we have all stopped vomming by then, you're on!"

And with that, I got the call that every Mother dreads after a night with their head over the bowl:

"Mummy, Jaime's just been sick all over herself..."

"Ed, gotta go my friend. Into the battle. See you on Saturday."

2 more nights of no sleep and one gorgeous child after the other, had turned themselves inside out. It is a form of hell, I am sure of it.

Saturday arrived and I looked like a dishcloth that had spent too long in bleach and had been left to dry in the sun. 36 hours of no sleep and clearing up sick meant that I was a strange green tinge and stunk of domestos. Hugely impressive for a first non date. It was a relief to be heading down to our little beach hut. It was my place of sanctity when my marriage first ended. Somehow being near the sea made me realise how insignificant my problems and me were. There was much more out there and once again, it was another thing that brought me hope.

We got to the hut, opened up, and the kids set up with paint brushes and paint to decorate the shingle and sat for a moment with my eyes closed, let the wind gently massage my face and for a moment everything was still. The washing machine is finished for now. Life has offered me some peace and some clarity. I don't know whether it was the sleep deprivation or the joy of being at my favourite place in the world but I could feel the tears slipping down my face. But for the first time in so long, these were happy tears.

It was just the best feeling in the world.

You see, one of the most magnificent things about being dealt a shit deck from time to time is that when you come out of the nightmare, albeit briefly, those moments of happiness are so much sharper and brighter than any normal joyous experience. They are breathtaking and memorable. Pain and despair has its upsides as it turns out.

I look at my watch. He is only half an hour late. I remember Eddie at college. I don't think he ever made a lesson on time. One of life's ditherers and procrastinators, always, always late. The day flew on and the clouds had started to come over and the kids were starting to get cold.
I looked at my watch again. 4 hours late??? Really Eddie? I had tried calling him on his mobile several times as I was mildly concerned that he might have either got lost or even worse had an accident, but it rang out. We were going to leave. Thunder and lightning was on its way and we were all terrified.

Packed up the hut and turned myself into my usual pack horse with two backpacks on, a beach bag in each hand and my handbag in my mouth (this shortage of limb issue really should be addressed for single mothers with small children by evolution I feel) and headed off towards the car. In the distance I see a man pushing a motorbike along the towpath. It couldn't be could it?

Torn between relief that he was ok and '4 fucking hours late, Ed?' I decided on relief when I saw that he had definitely had some kind of fall and was looking decidedly bedraggled himself.

"Blimey Ed, are you ok?"

"Yeah yeah, I am good thanks, so sorry I am so late..." his voice tailed off.

"What on earth has happened, you are covered in gravel... Crikey, you haven't come off that wretched thing have you?" (I hate motorbikes)

"Sort of. Look I am really sorry I have wrecked the day, can we not talk about it I am really fine."

He clearly wasn't.

"Eddie, just sit down."

We were all sat in the car park, surrounded by my 100's of bags and a rather battered looking motorbike and two spellbound children who are fascinated by this man who looks like an astronaut.

"Take off your helmet. What on earth has happened to you? Did you come off the bike?"

Such a stupid question. Of course he has, he is covered in gravel and the bike has a huge dent in the petrol tank.
No reply. Oh Christ, he might have some horrible head injury, delayed shock, about to keel over.

"Eddie, love, I'm worried what on earth has happened?"

"I had a little fall, came off the bike, but I'm fine."

"Look Ed, you are obviously NOT fine. A fall from a motorbike is NOT to be sneezed at. Let me get you to A&E, there's one literally just up the road from here. You need to get seen, you could have a concussion, internal bleeding... anything!"

"Em, I promise, I am fine, I am just tired from wheeling the bike here. Honestly, there is nothing wrong with me."

Would I give up? Would I buggery! I was going to show this man that I had compassion and could be counted on in an emergency. I bet his horrid ex-wife wasn't like that.

"Edward, I won't take no for an answer. This is serious. We are taking you to hospital."

The girls are thrilled. I had had quite a few stays in hospital since they were born and to them it meant hot chocolate and cake from the lobby shop.

"Em, no, I promise I am ok"

"How can you know that? You just came off a motorbike at speed! This is insane"

"Oh god, Em, I didn't come off at speed. I was stationary..."

Long silence.

"Stationary? How does that happen?"

"I was at those traffic lights about half a mile away and they finally went green. I took my feet off the ground and lost my balance and like some scene from Mr Bean I tipped sideways and in slow motion I ended up on the floor with the bike on top of me..."

A whole array of reactions were available to me at that point. A whole fucking array. Which one do I choose?

Hand over mouth, the giggling started. This slowly grew into hysterical laughter. I am now totally out of control. I snorted! Tears running down my face, shoulders shaking, wheezing slightly like Mutley. I haven't laughed like this for soooooooo long. The smile that spread across his face was like a rainbow under the ever-darkening skies. Something was sealed at that moment. We both knew it, we just didn't know what.

Eddie is not the tallest man in the world, this was his first trip out on his midlife crisis, post divorce self-gift and it was obviously way too big for him. But it was not only a gift for Eddie, it was a gift for me too.

"Nothing else for it my friend, you are going to have to leave that blasted thing here and come home with us!"

We spent one of the loveliest evenings, barbecuing outside in my little garden and we laughed with the kids until they went up to bed.

"Looks like I've met my match. Do you fall over a lot?"

"I don't actually, but if it means that I get to spend such a fantastic evening with 3 lovely ladies like this, then I am going to make more of a habit of it."

I waved his taxi off and I knew that something very special had just happened. For us both.

Chapter 13 - There's that reality thing again

Our little world kept on spinning. That seems to be how it is when you have two small children and a life that had been flung at you and your life had been turned on its head without warning. People used to ask me, "How do you do it? Two small kids, divorce, move to a new house, start again, try to survive on no money *and* keep smiling?"

The answer was always a simple one from me to them -

"I had no choice."

Of course, it was far more complicated than that in the day to day running of life as, not only a single mother, but as one as feckin hopeless as me!

But, today was a Monday. The day that most of the world loathes, but when you are a single parent with tiny children, weekends are times often to be dreaded. They are bleak, lonely and not the kind of gentle reminder that you are alone in this world and have fucked everything up, but the kind that hits you in the face like a shovel every hour or so. You find yourself drifting off into the opposite of a 'world of your own', but instead into a world that you wish was your own, the rest of the world had family time at the weekends. Nuclear families went out on day trips, had dinner parties, lived a normal and conventional life. Single parents often struggle with seeing that kind of normality. None of us set out to be alone with small children, it has either happened to us or we have failed. I chose the latter.

Things between Mike and me had settled since Chris had come on the scene, but not before he had had the opportunity to tell me why he had fallen out of love with me whilst I was pregnant with our gorgeous Jaime. Apparently, I changed when I got pregnant (no shit Sherlock!) Apparently, I stopped being a woman and became an incubator who was constantly ill and therefore lost my personality that he had married. When Abbie was born, I stopped being a wife and became only interested in my baby and was always too tired to be a proper wife to him. He explained, as time went on, he realised that he no longer saw me as a love interest, I was just someone who 'seemed like a good idea at the time'.

So, my life carried on with a divorce fought bitterly through the lawyers, a house move and here we were, living for the weekdays when most mothers were single and available for me to be with, and dreading the weekends. That was just how it went. The routine was a double-edged sword. It was comforting and made me feel safe, but in the same breath, having once been an 18 year old who took off around the world for a brief 6 months travelling, only to return 11 years later, it numbed me somehow.

Wake up, get kids ready for school, walk to school, deal with all the smiling faces talking about how fabulous their weekends had been, head down in case the tears came. Go to work, pick up kids, walk home, make tea, help with homework, bath time, bed (this is the longest part of the day - the bedtime ritual, takes about as long as the school day). Glass of wine. Bedtime with 2 little ones who have crept into your bed.

Repeat.
Repeat.
Repeat.

Working lunchtime shifts at a nearby pub brought some variety to my tiny tiny world which was a god send. I was of course fucking hopeless at everything. Thankfully, my boss was a treasure and often would invite his friends to come and have lunch in the pub just to witness Hurricane Emma drop glasses, fall over on spilt wine and drop fried eggs on more than one bald head. I soon became the pub entertainment, totally undeliberate, but it was a welcome break from just being Mummy.

Once a month the kids would have a weekend with Mike and Chris. This was also a tough one because even though it meant I had the opportunity to have some time to myself, I missed those little critters more than anything. We would meet halfway and for 24 hours my heart would be in my mouth and I would have butterflies when sitting in the layby waiting for their return.

In the past, my self-confidence was at such a low that I stayed at home and hid away from the world during those weekends, but now I had a little bit of hope in the form of Eddie.

We chose to take things very slowly and not to let the kids get involved just in case it all went tits up and they ended up getting hurt and abandoned all over again so now, these weekends were sometimes an absolute pleasure.

Being with Eddie on these occasions was like seeing purple and orange glow back in my life. It was warm and comforting. I was scared, so was he. All this was so unexpected and with both of us being so utterly feckin useless at relationships, it was often noted that we thought that we would protect each other from ourselves as we cared for each other so much. I am not going to deny that despite all my inner voices saying,

"Be careful Emma, you are in a relationship disaster, don't hurt this man, you are the LAST thing he needs at the moment."

I knew I was falling for him and there seemed to be little that I could do to stop it. I tried, I really did, but we were like best friends who never stopped laughing. The bit I could not get my head around was that this was a slow burn that seemed to be naturally growing into something really special, rather than all the others that start off with a massive 'fizz-bang' only to fizzle-bang out after a few months, or in my old marriage's case, It was a volcanic eruption of love and obsession from Mike's part only to freeze up overnight and never to come alive again.

I was far from knowing where I wanted this to go, but what I did know was that for now, this was perfect. That wonderful expression, 'this too will pass' is true of both bad and good things, and just when I thought I was in for a run of peace and quiet, another dreaded phone call from Chris.

"Emma, Emma, I am so so sorry to do this to you, but we're finished, I'm done, there's no trust. I don't know what to do, but I can't take much more of this..."

My heart broke for this poor lass. I felt grateful that I had not known about his, how shall I put it 'economic with the truth' until long after we had broken up. She was in the midst of it all and they were living in the same house and she was in love and her heart was breaking.

"Chris love, come down here. You need a break. Come and stay. The girls would love to see you and we can talk over a bottle of wine when they are in bed."

"Really? Really? You would do that for me?"

"Of course I would, I mean, blimey, who knows your situation and what you are going through better than me!?"

So Chris came down, she was thin, she was tired. She had been fighting a rare form of cancer (I had had that thrown in my face several times by Mike when he decided that he didn't want the children that weekend). The kids were made up. We tired them out as best we could, two Mums together and they finally went off to bed.

I looked at my friend, my replacement and with one last sigh of guilt, I was grateful for her pain. Not because I blamed her or revelled in her despair, but what he had done to her, had brought me the biggest sense of release from my emotional gymnastics that I had been tied up in for all my children's lives; I could stop blaming myself now.

She saw it. She had not just come here to be saved, she had come here to save me too. We both had tears pouring down our cheeks and we held each other for a good 5 minutes as two souls joined in mutual pain of being discarded. We talked the night away after that. There was laughter, tears, anger, revelations galore and that night, I knew that I got her through this as she too had got me through the past 6 years of having to hand over my precious children once a month.

Chris stayed for the night and then, reluctantly, she headed back up North to a torturous next few months. We all cried when she left. We didn't tell the girls why, just that I was going to miss my friend, but they would see her soon no doubt. Was that a bad lie to tell? Was it worse than Father Christmas or the Easter Bunny? The truth is, neither one of us knew what to say. We were winging it. As we had both discovered, my last 9 years and her 6 had been a myth. We just had to follow our instincts and trust in those.

Chapter 14 - Let the eavesdropping commence

The phone calls from Chris were frequent, changeable. Mike was full of regret and wanted her back. Selfishly I wanted them to work things out so that my girls could continue seeing their Dad whilst loving seeing their stepmother who was the main reason they went. They also adored her other favourite thing; her dog.

Eddie and I were now pretty much an item. We had 'come out' to the girls who adored him, and things were just so easy and straightforward with him. But when you looked at the situation from on high, it was not ideal. But hey, don't look a gift horse in the mouth. We all have our health and at the moment, things were all quiet on the western front and I was glad of that. Life has a habit of trundling along and you just get swept along for the ride. I had had a heavenly childhood and I fully intended to do the same for our little ones. Though, I hadn't quite factored in how bloody disorganised I actually was.

Primary school and all that goes with it is quite a bloody minefield. I had already proved myself to be a monumental cock up and was well known for turning up in the playground in my pyjama bottoms or with the kids in mismatched uniforms. It was all too much. Due to my deteriorating financial situation, I had been put in a position that my home working job was just simply not enough, so to add to my already totally chaotic life I got a job in a different pub as a barmaid doing a lunchtime shift.

That went well, turns out that I can drink like a pro on the other side of the bar, but taking orders, pouring drinks and getting food out to hungry and thirsty punters was not exactly my forte. Although, even though I was by far and away the oldest of the bar staff, I was mothered and protected by my younger colleagues and as it turns out I became a bit of a local attraction. Not in the way that you might think... no no no, I was like an urban myth, when Emma was behind the bar, anything could and nearly always DID happen.

As a result, I somehow managed to keep my job for a few months as I brought in a few extra customers who genuinely thought I was the entertainment.

"Oh please can you do the 'dropping the fried egg on the bald man's head' thing again - so funny.'"
"Uh, who told you about that? It was a very greasy fried egg and the poor man is much better now and the burn mark has nearly gone now."

"Please can you make my friend one of your special Bloody Mary's? You know the ones where you get distracted and just pouring the Tabasco in? We've still got your last effort on film, bloody brilliant!"

Daily glass smashes and getting food orders wrong, racing around the pub garden barefoot because I had so many blisters on my feet, shouting for my next victims to show themselves as I had their food which I was just about to drop, was all getting a bit much for this decrepit antique. I had to make another plan.

I used to race to the school playground after one of these insane shifts at this fabulous establishment, which only just survived Emma on a daily basis, often sprinting from the car as I was almost late only to just arrive as Jaime and Abbie came flying out of their classrooms into my awaiting arms as I scooped down to their level. We would hug each other for a matter of minutes and then I would be bombarded with stories of what had happened to them on their separate days at this wonderful little school. I would look at these two excited, innocent, totally adorable little faces, and their voices that were competing for my attention were blurred into the background as I realised slowly that I had absolutely no fucking way to get back up again. The knees had locked, and all the other parents were meeting and greeting their little ones too.

I was exhausted beyond belief and as I looked into my little girl's eyes, desperately wanting to be able to remember what the feck they were telling me about their time in the herb garden, I was still in a panic as to how the bloody hell I was going to get up from this. And then it happened. Eddie came up behind me and put both arms under mine and lifted me out of my body trap and the girls went wild to see him. Total surprise. The best surprise. So why was I crying? Please don't let the girls see. Please don't let the rest of the playground see. Please don't let anyone see that I am failing.

I am barely keeping my head above water and I don't know how much longer my smile will last let alone my bloody knees! Eddie got it. He somehow had picked up from one of my phone calls that my parental tether was coming to an end and I physically was shot.

He didn't make a fuss, he slipped me his hanky so I could dry my eyes and he whisked the girls off to get an ice cream at the village shop and I followed behind, dragging my knees, ankles and blistered feet behind me.

Something had to change.

We sat up into the early hours of the morning discussing how things had gotten this bad and how I was basically heading into the burnout zone. Two small children, no money, a job designed for someone 20 years younger than me and me with the organisational skills of a toothpick, something HAD to give. One thing I have learned since becoming a mother, not just a single mother, but just a mother, is that kids will take you to the brink of insanity to where you think -

"Holy mother of God, I cannot fucking do this anymore!!!" and you're there. You are really there. You are at the end of your sanity and are about to have yourself that nervous breakdown which has been threatening since they were born, and then, at that precise moment when you really can take no more, something changes. It stops. You are onto something different. A new phase of growing up, with its new set of problems and coping strategies, but it has changed. You can cope with this one. Until you can't. But for now, the change has come, and it is the dawn of a new chapter.

So shifts reduced slightly, and I was on the lookout for something more appropriate. Two of my favourite customers come to the bar several times a week. Lunch at *The Horse* was the perfect place to discuss business and I had decided that I was going to stop being a total feckin buffoon, stop slipping over in the restaurant area and wearing the most expensive cuts of beef with mushroom sauce, that was all behind me now. I was going to become a spy and a job sleuth and be a fantastic professional.

"Hi gents, how are we doing today?"

"Yeah, Emma, all good thanks, how are you?"

"Yep, I am all good, definitely going to get your drinks the right way around and none of this gravy on the salad malarky anymore. I am a new woman."

"How dreadfully disappointing, you're the only reason we come into this joint, it's free entertainment and the food is always a delicious and an interesting surprise."

"Yes, well I am leaving her behind me, I am a consummate professional now, on the lookout for a new job where I am not a hazard to the general public and I can use some of my other skills, you know the ones that don't involve balancing things on my head or doing anything at any kind of speed."

To my utter disbelief and pleasure, these two gorgeous gents looked at each other, one raised an eyebrow and the other one tipped his head to one side and they both nodded.

Andy spoke first,

"I think we might have just the thing for you, Emma, would you come and meet our other lovely CEO and perhaps you two can chat?"

"Uh yes yes yes!" and I ever so professionally ran around to the side of the bar that I should always have stayed on and hugged them both.

And so, a road safety officer was born. Right there and then. It was perfect. Used all my skills of embarrassing myself in public, ranting about terrible people driving and reversing into things all at the same time!

This moment was the start of a new Emma. An Emma that could start to see her way out of the darkness of living with no money, no energy and no self-respect. This was it. The end of the awful washing machine. But, of course it wasn't. It never quite is.

Chapter 15 - Getting a puppy and a hysterectomy in one month...

Apparently, in that instant, everything goes tits up and you regret your smugness within minutes. But I was making an exception today. I was holding my first road safety workshop for some really lovely firefighters and I felt amazing. I was using my redundant and truly rusty brain again and it was like someone had put me in a warm shower on a cold day. I was back. No more cleaning toilets, no more nappy changing, no more getting drinks orders wrong, no more relentless CBeebies, no more blisters on my bare feet, no more crying at the kitchen sink with exhaustion and boredom combined. The light at the end of the tunnel was not a train, it was the new me.

Working Mum with a job to be proud of.

Working Mum with two amazing daughters who were happy and settled.

Working Mum with a steady boyfriend who she loved and who loved her, and her girls.

Working single Mum who had a great working relationship with her children's father.

There it was, my single biggest accomplishment in this whole episode of my life. I had done it. We had done it. We had navigated some really choppy waters where some of the lies that Mike had told me, I thought I would never be able to get past. Some of the extraordinary criticisms that had been levelled my way, I really believed, and I hated him for putting me in the situation where I was destined to fail. He knew I was hopeless and just when I was least expecting it, he would take my knees out and knock me down. He'd let me get back up of course, I had a job to do, but when it looked like I was doing just a tad too well, out came that crow bar again and knees at the ready.

But life went on. It does that. And here I was.

So, was I going to let this newfound status quo stick around? Was I buggery! Let me tell you, although I had found a new setting on my washing machine lifestyle, I still had rather a lot on my plate still. In short, I was burnt out, knackered, broke and exhausted. I had a day job, 2 small children, a boyfriend who lived in London, so was basically still a single mum. I spent most of my life heading for meetings that I was supposed to be at the following week. I was often to be found in the school office blaming my CRAFT disease for my latest fuck up with permission slips which meant that my little gits couldn't go to Legoland or something and the rest of the time I was setting fire to one meal or another.

I was STILL struggling.

I knew I had to make a change. I had to do something to take away some of the pressure from my quickly unravelling sanity.

What should I do? Or more to the point, what did I do? Let me tell you what I did.

I got a puppy.

A delicious, gorgeous, totally edible and as it turns out, completely untrainable labrador puppy.

Spencer was here and life was never going to be the same again. Abbie and Jaime were beside themselves and although he arrived as if butter wouldn't melt in that perfect little mouth of his, before long, he had eaten the kitchen floor, the cat flap, most of the front door and then he moved on to parts of the village. Within a few months he had been shoplifting all the bread from the village shop. He nearly killed me outside a very smart man's house, where I had tied his lead around my neck whilst casually talking to a very abrupt man who was rather scathing about how badly behaved my puppy was. Only to be proved right as Spencer the bastard dog took off like Concorde basically garrotting me in the process and as all the colour drained from my face and my lips went blue, all the posh man could say was-

"Ooooh, who needs to go to puppy school?"

Once I had actually reached a rather gorgeous purple/puce colour, he realised I was actually dying and let Spencer off the lead to pursue his cat as it turns out who was sent scuttling off into his perfect garden breaking a load of pots as he went.

Not sorry.

The next memorable occasion was when I unhooked the fecker off the gate posts outside the school, assumed my usual 'bendzeeknee' water skiing position as he loved to use that precise moment to cart me off down the street, but not this time, oh no. Spencer was on point for this moment. His collar snapped, he fucked off at great speed totally unrestrained towards the village pub, leaving me momentarily stock still, looking like someone had removed a chair from underneath me and the film had been paused, to then do what physics demanded which was to fall backwards, arse first into the school hedge which as luck would have it was full of thorns.

Who was there to fish me out? The headmistress.

"You again Emma, how's the puppy training going?"

Spencer was already ordering his first pint by the time I got myself out of the hedge.
But, despite being a criminal, a thief who stole ALL foods ranging from Big Macs out of delivery driver's vans to eating an entire chicken pie off my kitchen table just before a load of guests arrived and then throwing it all back up in the hallway.

So, I had managed, quite beautifully, to complicate our lives a little further and add to my stress levels. But, when you have no other choice and you decided a few years back that your children come first, you do crazy things like acquire a totally untrainable Labrador pup and try and hold down a fairly serious job in road safety.

But, hey, I was invincible, I could do this! In fact, my bosses (god bless their deluded souls) had such faith in me that they sent the biggest fuck up in the West (that would be me) up to an extremely important conference made up of EVERY SINGLE CHIEF FIRE OFFICER in the country as one of the main presenters of a brand new, pioneering software programme for all young drivers.

Yep, I am as surprised as you, but there you are, off I headed to a destination up North about 4 hours away for an 8.30am start to set up all my paraphernalia and talk 'saving young lives' to about 200 extremely influential men and women. The 4am start was a joy. Lots of coffee beforehand meant that by the time I had hit the 1 hour mark I was bursting for the loo. Whizzed into the next service station on the M1 and had a 'whizz' and out I came. Got back in the car, looked in my rear-view mirror and to my absolute horror, in the boot, there he was: Spencer. The feckin dog! The little shit must have hopped in so quietly as I was loading up and decided he too was going to be a part of my first truly professional presentation since 2002. Oh holy fuck, what the bloody hell was I supposed to do?

Only one thing for it, onwards and upwards – literally – Telford bound with 40kgs of dog with me, in my best suit. I was met at 8am by my favourite CFO who I had to sheepishly explain about my travelling companion. Thankfully he found the whole situation hilarious and said that there were plenty of fire officers that would walk the boy around a field whilst I attempted to blow the minds of the UK's Fire Service with this amazing new brain training software programme.

Would Spencer leave my side? That would be a very large NO. He pulled and pulled and eventually lay down in the car park and barked relentlessly until we agreed that he'd be better off where he could at least see me, albeit through the window of the conference hall. But no, that was not enough for this deranged animal. In short, my entire powerpoint presentation that I had worked on, practised to within an inch of my life was delivered with my insane canine sitting by my side, farting and whining to the point that I even asked for one of their gas masks that were on display in the foyer. It was an unmitigated disaster, but one that turned out to work in my favour. Spencer and I were apparently an unforgettable duo who had brought a bit of sunshine and fun to what was normally a rather dull affair.

On our long journey home, I had a small epiphany – this is often not a good thing, people have been known to take cover when I announce that something extraordinary had come to my mind, but on this occasion I thought, maybe, just maybe, this walking catastrophe MIGHT just be onto something.

I decided that I would NOT in fact remove the 'EPIC FAILURE' stamp that had been permanently tattooed across my forehead, but I would, instead, highlight it, colour it, enlarge and more importantly start writing about it. And so, a small movement was born. My daft little blog.

I gently recovered from my mortifying experience at the Fire Service conference and was reassured that Spencer's performance was nearly as good as my own and was note-worthy. Maybe there really was something to be said for being 'unforgettable for all the wrong reasons'. It was 2012 and what was to come was definitely worth writing about, if for no other end, no-one would believe me if I didn't document it.

Life carried on. Permission slips were forgotten, I attended school assemblies in my pyjamas because I got the wrong Friday for red nose day, CRAFT disease in full swing and the kids kept me busy with their antics with the mad dog. He had continued to basically eat the house and I had given the girls the job of coming up with appropriate punishments for him. One was pretty memorable.

We had a trampoline in the front garden which they decided to put him on for a doggy bounce on a regular basis, on this occasion, fully dressed in ALL my underwear, bra, french knickers and, god help me, a garter belt. He was quite a show piece for the village that day, and I decided not to leave the house for about 3 months. But, there we were. We were trundling along, something that I truly never believed would happen. I thought my life was going to be one battle after another with Mike, but so far so good.

My Mum had always given me some rather fabulous nuggets of advice over the years and on that day, she could not have been more right. I had been experiencing some rather unpleasant stomach pains over the months preceding and I was advised to go and see my GP.

He had sent me for some routine blood tests and told me it was nothing to worry about. I was called in for the results, something which once again I was not overly concerned about, until the GP in question looked up at me and in a rather monotonic way said

"Oh dear, it looks as if you have tested positive for ovarian cancer..."

His words didn't drop into the air as they do in most stories, they were fired at me with a water cannon, knocking me off my feet. I had NO idea I had even been tested for this?! There had to be some mistake??? For quite some time – about 3 minutes I think – I stopped breathing. I stopped talking. In fact, everything stopped, I believe my heart did for a few seconds.

"Um, could you please ask someone to take the girls into reception, I think I have some questions for you Dr?"

I had to wait 4 days for a scan to find out how advanced this cancer was. The longest 4 days of my life by far. As it turned out, my elevated CA125 level was a false positive and all was well, just a mystery of modern science. But, the shockwaves that moment in the Dr's surgery and the days that had followed had sent through me, had changed everything. I wanted this investigated and dealt with. The GP, having realised his mistake, agreed. In short, I was sent to see a consultant who I begged to remove anything that may possibly go wrong in that department and so my hysterectomy and ovary removal was booked.

Now, for anyone else that would have been a fairly straightforward procedure, but for this walking wally, there was always going to be some incident or another. I arrived for my scheduled hysterectomy to be confronted with a plastic cup. My premature elation that they were putting me straight onto those fabulous 'dancing on the ceiling' medication was somewhat subdued when I was asked to provide a sample to ensure that I was not in fact 'with child' which could have been a nasty surprise for us all, child included!

So, I dutifully went and filled up the little cup (how do people judge these things, I needed a 2-litre coke bottle!) I put it in the bin whilst I got my draws back up.

Washed my hands like a good catholic girl, then used the super hygienic pull-paper to dry off the ol' mits and then stepped decisively on the foot operated bin whose lid of course, as it should, flew upwards, sending my sample flying up the wall and all over my new tunic.

Oh, FFS Emma, why you?! Why is it always you?! So, I go to flush the loo again to try and get the ol' juices going so I can produce another sample and very quickly discover that I have in fact pulled the panic alarm and within seconds I was surrounded by nurses, porters, one junior doctor and my mortified other half. Not in any true distress just staring aimlessly at my somewhat tasteless artwork all over the loo wall and desperately trying to pretend that I was soaked because of an over vigorous tap. Totally convinced I had got away with my latest misdemeanour; I threw back my pee covered hair and waltzed off to my bed with my sizeable derriere on full display as Ed had forgotten to tie the back up.

It can safely be said that the nursing staff were glad to see the back of me (not literally) when I finally left. I had been warned before my operation that a gradual slide into the menopause as most women experience, was not what was going to happen to me, oh no. I was going to basically get on an Emma-made bob-sledge and fly into it out of control and finally hit the brick wall of all brick walls.

Ah menopause-sch menopause – I had this! Or so I thought...

Chapter 16 - The start of the big M

Welcome oh welcome, Emma, to single motherhood and the surgical menopause. This was an eye opener even for me, who had assumed that she had experienced every emotion, every cock up, every dark place known to man. How WRONG could I have been. This was a whole new kettle of fish and came laced with some of the most extraordinary and unexplainable symptoms. I, of course, had been warned about the hot flushes, the mood swings (mine's chains had snapped long ago) but no-one had mentioned that your brain leaves the building pretty interminably, you have the memory of a toothpick and you have absolutely ZERO control over what comes out of your mouth and even less of what goes into your brain. For someone who had already proved herself to be a walking liability, this was truly worrying.

However, with my epiphany of diarising all my epic failures underway, this was a grand opportunity to really get some great material down on paper. I had NO idea what was about to happen, neither did those around me… and so, The Menopausal Mayhem Mothers was well and truly born and about to take the world or social media by storm and wipe me off my feet.

But before we get into that, I have to tell you of the start of my journey out of hysterectomy recovery and into the world of surgical menopause. I have always been a somewhat bloody-minded person at the best of times, even worse at the worst of times, so I was pretty damned determined that this Menopause thingy was NOT going to get this girl down. I was invited into the girls' school to do a short talk on road safety much to my daughters' utter mortification. On arrival I said my hellos to the class, most of whom knew me from the playground, when one little lad piped up,

"Morning Mrs Gardner, hope you are feeling better after your operation, what did you have done?"

I looked quizzically at the teacher as to whether I should reply or just by-pass the question, but definitely got the nod that I should briefly explain.

That teacher has a lot to answer for in terms of (a) my new discovery of no brain to mouth filter and (b) my short-term relationship with my daughters.

My reply to this sweet young man's question was

"Well Alfie, um, in short, I have basically been spayed..."

The road safety talk went as well as you can imagine with absolutely none of the children able to maintain any form of concentration after that and neither of my children seemed to be able to prise their heads off their desks for the duration of my short but definitely memorable visit.

And so it had begun. A new step up into the world of Emma gaffs.

A few months after my operation, I did start to notice that my normally good-natured demeanour had the ability to do an 'Incredible Hulk', or as my other half started to call it, as the menopausal weight piled on, an 'Incredible Bulk', on me. I could do from mild mannered and amiable to "fuck with me at your peril" in pretty much the blink of an eye. Case in point, a short visit to our local amenity tip. How was I to know that you had to take an ID to prove that you live in the area to drop your 4,000 bottles of wine off in their skip? Seems they need to know which is the most alcoholic region in the south east. Reckon I would have just cleared that up that little mystery for them - but not as easily as you'd think...

Yes, I had no idea that ID was required, or as the lovely gents at the gate mentioned a utility bill of some kind - hmmmm, yes, I am prone to hiding gas bills in my handbag just in case of a moment like this. Then it hit me, I owned the biggest skip of all AND I had it on me! My handbag! Lightbulb moment! There were receipts galore, a half eaten apple, oooh and a petrol voucher - expired - surprise surprise - ah, from 2017...

Then finally, at the bottom of the shithole, I finally find a bit of A4 paper that is definitely looking like a bill of some kind. Genius. Yes yes, there it is, my name in the corner, my address.
With the smuggest smile on my face I hand them my 'utility bill.'

"There you go boys, see, I pay for my electric and everything AND I do it from the next village."

I was absolutely thrilled.

As I was handing it over to the lovely Polish gentleman, to my horror I saw the letters at the top right hand corner of the said electricity bill: NHS

And then: "Your next scheduled smear test is..."

Oh no.
Kill me now.

I wouldn't mind but the NHS had actually removed my bloody cervix only months before! Oh how all the four of us laughed. Yes, quite a crowd had gathered as I was rummaging through my handbag. Apparently, there'd been quite a bit of hostility at the gate when people turn up without their smear test appointment letters, so any sign of trouble and the heavy mob appear. The brain-mouth lack of filter appeared again, I actually explained the letter to them. In detail! Shit feck bollocks Emma, this is getting out of hand.

Totally flummoxed by my total weirdness, the poor man at the gate shepherded me on through and on I went to the array of different categories of skips. Now THIS is my nemesis.

Logic.

Car heaped to the gills with empty wine bottles, SO much old shit from an old oil can to a mattress, a load of old bedding and so many cardboard boxes I could have become a children's entertainer and an old broken garden fork. I reverse up, trying to look all confident and that I know what I am doing. Get out one bag and get stopped by a rather attractive Polish man who said I was in the wrong bay and needed to go to line 5. I was hugely apologetic as this was obviously his area of expertise and most certainly not mine.

I had discovered long before my hysterectomy that I literally do NOT have an ounce of common sense in me anywhere. Trust me, I have looked, as have others. The next thing I hear a similar exchange with the lovely Polish gentleman and an elderly local where basically the old boy had done the same as me, gone to the wrong skip basically, easy mistake to make, glad to be corrected. But was this guy pleased?

Oh no, he was about as pleased as I was when Spencer rolled in a HUGE pile of fox shit at our local pub and proceeded to race around the pub spreading his newfound, award winning scent. This old boy was bloody FUMING! He then proceeded into a tirade of abuse on this poor young lad. Well, my newfound menopausal hormones kicked in. I was not having this...

"Oi! Oi!"

Christ on a bike, I had my beanie and wellies on and my 'meno face', and was SO not to be messed with.

"He is only doing his job you miserable old bastard, why can't you just be nice!?!"

I don't think anyone had ever stood up to this old codger before because the man looked positively terrified. He stamped one foot, shouted something that I couldn't quite understand and threw his strimmer on the floor and marched off. Both the young man he had shouted at and I looked at each other in disbelief, not really sure what to say, until he broke the silence and said in slightly broken English,

"Blimey, no-one ever speaks to my Uncle like that, you brave lady".

I was completely taken aback. Where had this newfound anger come from? He was right, was I brave or was I in fact totally and utterly deranged? This was new to me and the fact that the bloke was indeed related to the nice young polish chap had skimmed over my head as I tried to process what I had just done. But I needed to finish off my tip run and just when I thought, things can't possibly get any worse, I pulled myself together and promptly threw my final bin bag into the "household waste' skip and watched my car keys shine brightly as they flew into the air and drifted gracefully alongside my last ounce of dignity.

It was strange because I took some sort of comfort from my final Emma-ism. THAT I was used to, but the turning green and almost expecting all my clothes to start ripping as I took on curmudgeonly pensioner was a new one on me, and really rather disturbing. Not just for me as it turns out, he and his nephew looked positively relieved as I departed the tip with my empty car and my temper back under control.

Other weird things started to happen. My memory had definitely started to deteriorate. I seemed to be spending 50% of my life looking for things that I had lost. Things like car keys. They became like biros or fag lighters, they did magical disappearing acts, all at the wrong times. On one particular occasion I was scrabbling around the old skip – better known as my handbag – when I came across a random chicken fillet breast wrapped in cling film. What the actual... ahhhhhhhh, I knew instantly where my car keys were. Freezer. And blow me down I was only bloody right! There were other experiences, just another normal school morning, massive row with our eldest on the doorstep, me dressed as a large rabbit (only onesie I could lay my hands on) about the fact that I tidied her shit tip of a room yesterday and appear to have thrown away ALL of her school books. This, of course, was only noticed 30 seconds before she left for school and was very loudly announced to the whole neighbourhood that not only had I "stolen" her school books to get her into trouble but also by arguing with her I was in fact preventing her from going to school which is a criminal offence.

Please keep bearing in mind that she is addressing a large rabbit at this point.

Whilst all this is going on, and the curtains are twitching wildly by now, the feckin dog has escaped and once the vile and violated teenager had in fact left the scene of my dreadful crime, I see the bastard labrador curling out what can only be described as a volcano sized crap on my opposite neighbour's lawn. Oh, holy mother of God. I would be livid if I was them. So, without a moment's thought, I grab a load of dog crap bags and head over the road to correct this abomination. The lovely family, who had only moved in recently so were blissfully unaware that their neighbour was indeed a total lunatic, had several teenagers who appeared at the precise moment that an enormous rabbit was on their lawn picking up the largest, steaming turd you have ever seen.

Yes, I had forgotten to get dressed.
Our eyes met. And then in kicked the brain to mouth problem and I uttered the immortal words,

"It wasn't me..."

If there was indeed an evaporation button available to ALL menopausal women, I would have used it right there and then.

Chapter 17 - The MMM

I was reminded of this very fact one sunny day in some or another year in from 2013 on
I was happily pottering around on the driveway when Eddie came up behind me and whispered quietly in my ear

"You are not going to bloody believe this Em, that bloke from Fifty Shades of Grey is on the green!"

"No way! You are feckin kidding me?! - you bastard, you ARE feckin kidding me."

"Em, seriously, go and look for yourself, he's out there with his kids playing football on the green right now!"

OMFG. Jamie Dornan is within 100m of me. I can't possibly go and look at him myself so I drag my eldest daughter who has the body of a goddess and I attempt to hide myself behind her as I steer her in the direction of the green under the pretence we are looking for the dog.

Two bloody things foiled our brilliant and subtle plan.

1. I wasn't wearing my glasses so I couldn't bloody see him.

2. SPENCER! He only comes running up behind us and fucks up the whole 'we have lost our dog' thing.

Nothing else for it, got to come clean. So, I emerge, red faced and mortified. Him and his kids are looking at me like I have lost me bloody marbles because Georgie had buggered off by then realising, I had been massively wound up and this was just a man with a super sexy Northern Irish accent.

So, what would a normal person do? Walk away right.

Oh, not me. No no no, I have to try and explain what the fuck I was up to. I strolled over trying my hardest to look cool. Epic fail. Then proceeded to tell him that my bastard other half had wound me up bla bla bla. Well, he was lovely about it.

Thought it was very funny and said that it happens quite a lot, which was unsurprising because this man was seriously HOT! So, there we are standing on the green having a good ol' chat about life and kids, how much I hate my other half and am planning on leaving him after this latest little ha ha not funny joke - and I realise, OMG, I am actually flirting with this man! I look to my right to our driveway and there is Eddie and my daughters absolutely hosing themselves with laughter.

Ah, they think I am still explaining the wind up, well more fucking fool them! I am having the time of my life throwing my middle-aged self at this gorgeous creature. He was SO charming and actually really caring and seemed quite protective of me. SO sweet! Surely, they can see I am flirting my fat arse off? So why the fuck is the beloved not getting annoyed and the girls not rolling their eyes? No, they are still fucking laughing. I'll bloody show them. It was SO screamingly obvious that this guy was enjoying our little dalliance as he was laughing at all my silly jokes and little innuendos that I was lapping it all up. Bloody marvellous, I was back on the dating scene and ALL of it in front of my family! No nasty cheating or sneaking around, right there in full view of them all. WTF they found so funny about the whole thing is beyond me at this point in time.

Anyway, like all fabulous things, it had to come to an end. His kids were looking well awkward, and I guess I had had my time so I bid him a fond farewell and swaggered back to the driveway.

"All right you lot, you thought you had got one over on me, well I bloody showed you, didn't I?! This ol girl has still got it!"

"Yes, love, you definitely have still got it. The only problem is you used it without your trousers on."

I looked down and to my utter horror he was right. I was not wearing any trousers and what was even worse was the thundercrackers that I had on were so feckin old and huge they actually had holes in...

Another 'where is my evaporation button moment'. But was this all down to the menopause? I had definitely noticed of late that I had started meeting and greeting delivery drivers at the front door with no trousers on – on one occasion I was even LESS clothed, tragically for me the dog managed to escape past me as I realised my rather sporting error and did manage to hide behind the door.

Sadly, and rather quickly FORGOT my situation of having just stepped out of the shower and was, how shall I put this, towel clad, and went in hot pursuit of the beast in order to avoid another 'peaking turd' moment on our long suffering neighbour's lawn, got the towel caught on the handle of the door and proceeded to leave the building totally in the buff with Spencer's rear end heading off to his new local toilet. For once, luck was on my side and the delivery man had turned on his heel and was on his way to his van and it was extremely early. My first, but sadly NOT last, attempt at sporting naturism had gone unnoticed but this was becoming a rather too regular occurrence for my liking.

My memory loss was a source of endless embarrassment and degradation in my life. Case in point, here is how my days can spiral downwards at quite a rate of knots: So, on one particular occasion, Eddie worked from home (something I normally hate as it involves a LOT of criticism and observation of how I use MY working day) but I thought, no, think positive, get the fecker out on a run with me. We aim to go quite a long way which he is thrilled about as he is far fitter than I am. A couple of miles in and we are chatting away about schools, the kids etc when it suddenly bloody dawns on me that I have a meeting with the deputy head at 10am.

I know I could have done this differently, but this is me, so that was never going to happen. So, after a whole load of expletives, shouting and shit fuck shit fuck shit fuck (can you even imagine the other 'expletives' if I have to refer to them as such?). So, the usual from the ever supportive and understanding boyfriend, "Oh FFS Emma, you are feckin hopeless". "When are you going to stop being such a clutterfuck and start organising yourself better? I mean, if you're not racing around because you've forgotten where you're supposed to be, then you are flying around the house trying to find all the shit you've lost!" I had to endure the sanctimonious swine the whole way back.

By the time we got to the front door, I had seriously had enough and shouted at him:

"Will you just remember who you are talking to and go and find your manners!"

I know this is not going to get me very far as I am dealing with the MOST organised person on planet earth. All he could say in return was,

"Find my manners? Find my bloody manners? Don't tell me you've gone and bloody lost those too?"

– this was the point that the Menopause kicked in and so did my running shoe, straight between the fecker's buttocks and off he went, shoe up his arse, into the downstairs lav where I restrained him by holding the door shut. So so so childish, but suddenly this had become fun. I was as silent as a little mouse, so he actually thought I had in fact locked him in from the outside and had left. It took every bone in my body to not ruin the joke by giggling. Oh, the joy of hearing him shouting

"Yeah, all right Em, joke over, I've got a lot to do, you can let me out now, sorry for saying you are a clutterfuck."

(as I am right by the door with my foot against it I can still hear him whisper under his breath):

"but you fecking are"

– so that's another two minutes in khazi custody.) But the beauty, oh the divine poetry of this totally unplanned punishment is that I have realised that all I have to do is walk away quietly and as he has been intermittently shoving the door to no avail (I am a strong unit let me tell you) when I have let go, he is going to chuck his shoulder into his cell door and come flying out unrestrained he's going to definitely definitely fall over.

And today, oh beautiful, beautiful day, it happens. Mr Bloody Organised, gives the bog door one last shoulder thrust and there is no resistance at all, and he shoots out like a magician from a cannon and lands face first in the hallway. My position of legs crossed like a naughty school girl with tears pouring down my cheeks did nothing to detract from his fury. I have to let the dust settle, walk away. I've also slightly taken my eye off the ball that I have this appointment with the Deputy Head which is the reason we had to curtail our run together in the first place and lead to Ed's incarceration. So, shower, brush hair, suit and boot and off I go. Back 20 minutes later. Husband calmed down, has seen the funny side of the situation and was JUST about to apologise for ridiculing my chaos when he uttered those immortal words,

"Why are you back so quickly?" Oh bollocks. Can't lie, can't because then you have to remember stuff. So here it came. Why is my fun ALWAYS so short lived?

"Got the wrong day, the meeting is tomorrow..."

Chapter 18 - SPENCER!

Memory loss was one thing, and it was causing me endless mortifying experiences, but there were other factors that combined with my newly acquired brain fog and my natural ability to make a total twat of myself that seemed to be building in frequency and I felt I was slowly becoming socially unpalatable. I tried blaming everything on the dog, which in many cases was wise as he was a total liability.

One of my favourite things was heading down to our local pub with a girlfriend and putting the world to rights. It's just one of those rights of passage when you have kids and you need a bloody break from the four walls that have become not only a place of work, but well, your place of work! Churning out meal after meal, endless washing that makes you question whether there are actually people that live in your house that you have not met yet and relentless tidying as if you were a member of staff at a party you never attended. So, there it was, a beautiful sun drenched Friday evening and my friend Laura and I took our moment and ran with it. One small error of judgement was looking into those big, brown, soulful eyes of my beautiful dog and giving in. Yes, I took him with us. Our quiet and relaxing evening of winding down did NOT go to plan and ended up with Spencer getting banned from our local pub.

It all began with the absolutely stomach-churning moment when he appeared from the field at the end of the pub garden whilst all the happy diners were enjoying their lovely Friday evening meal in the July sunshine, with a live rabbit in his mouth. I did, of course, apologise profusely to everyone whose kids were screaming in distress whilst their parents were trying to comfort them at the same time as gagging on their burgers. Rather stupidly I thought it would be a good idea to try and catch the fecker, but this is his favourite game and to everyone's horror rather than amusement a display of 49 year old woman, body seen better days, lumbering after an extremely nimble labrador who could outrun a New Zealand winger any day of the week, was just too much.

I, of course, fell several times, mainly over the dog, perhaps a couple of kids too, it was utter carnage. Some lovely young lad took pity on me and joined the chase but to no avail and Spencer ended up dismembering the poor rabbit very publicly, very noisily and very very fucking slowly.

I'm not going to lie; it was pure agony. Not for the rabbit, sadly that had gone to the rainbow bridge (or so I tried to frantically tell the onlooking screaming children), no, the agony was all mine. This could NOT get any worse... or could it? It was when the wretched beast returned to our table looking seriously sheepish and guilty to then regurgitate Flumper, WHOLE, into my handbag... Laura and I left, very quickly. Evening ruined.

Now most normal people would actually learn a lesson from this excruciating situation, but the menopause is a bit like childbirth. At the time the pain and the indignity are overwhelming, but some kind of chemical is apparently produced in your brain so that you forget the experience and go on to reproduce again. Well, just like that, so apparently do moments like these public disgraces. Yes, I did it again and again. Took either a handful of girlfriends or the family armed with Spencer who was like an out-of-control toddler. Our lovely local landlord, who had, in all fairness, given Spencer and me more chances than we deserve, and had overlooked so many of our debacles but when he had had enough, he had had enough and it was the moment that I heard the dulcet tones of his gorgeous Scottish accent screaming from the patio,

"Emma, get your feckin dog out of my kitchen!!!"

Yet another moment where I hung my head in shame, but lesson STILL not learned I took it upon myself to plead for Spencer's stay of execution and to please give us both one more chance. Quite rightly, the landlord said that we could indeed HAVE that chance if I kept the bugger on a lead.

So, a gorgeous August Friday evening presented itself and Kate and I headed off down to the pub with Spencer all suited and booted (well collar and lead) and ordered our first delicious bottle of crisp, cold Sauvignon Blanc. 3 times. In the first 15 minutes. 3 feckin times that dog pulled me off the pub garden bench backwards. I was like a bloody enormous ladybird on my back, flapping about trying to get vertical again.

If I actually had stomach muscles and a waist, it might have been more elegant, but on all three occasions I needed assistance. Very bloody glamorous. So, my dear friend suggested that, rather than trying to hold this evil beast myself, every time a plate of cheesy chips came out, I should tie him to the table.

This sadly was Spencer's and my undoing. For the next plate of bloody chips that came out saw 40kg of dog begin to drag 2 fully grown women, an entire table and benches all connected and the contents of the precious bottle of SB across the pub garden. It was unbelievable. We made it about 10 metres until the whole shebang became dismantled and we all ended up in a heap on the floor with Spencer, finally free, with only a now detached bench flying behind him to beg for the chips. Kate and I were on our bellies on the grass, the table and ONE bench were upside down and the bottle was smashed.

His ban was final.
He's totally blown it.

Although, we did get a huge round of applause from some visiting people who thought we were the pub entertainment.

So, with my name firmly established as the village clown, I carried on with this worrying thought still in the back of my head. Am I normal? Is this state of affairs normal? Or is it the new found joys of the rollercoaster ride that was the menopause? My decision-making process was decidedly dodgy, I had proven that, but really? Was this how it was to be for the foreseeable?

In the midst of all this chaos, Eddie had proposed to me and I had said yes and we bought a house together. In many ways, having gone through one of the darkest chapters of my life, where the terror of an uncertain future and the prospect of being a single mother forever and failing my beautiful daughters was a blessing, as was this new stability – well a lovely home and wonderful boyfriend – was so appreciated and on a daily basis, but there was still this nagging doubt that I was indeed going totally and utterly mad. I needed some help.

So off to the GP I toddled and told him that my anxiety levels were through the roof, I often felt like murdering random people and my memory was so bad that I had headed off to the vet to get Spencer his annual vaccinations and had ended up, standing at the reception desk of the surgery without the bloody dog! My long-suffering GP put this down to a form of anxiety driven depression and I was put on a course of antidepressants. A fat lot of good they did to me, I got worse if anything. And once again I blamed the dog!

As the menopause began to progress, and as I was at a younger age than your average menopausal woman, I was horrified by some of the physical aspects of the "change" as my mother liked to call it. I used to wash my hair and great clumps would start falling out. Of course, being a Labrador owner, I assumed, as it was spring by then, I was indeed malting like the rest of the world, but my hair started to thin at an alarming rate. Then my teeth started to give me jip.

I had always had a fairly good pair of gnashers, sturdy and fairly low maintenance. In fact they were such a prominent feature, Eddie once made the mistake when I asked him who my "doppelganger would be" - evidently hoping for someone like Kim Bassinger or at best the newsreader Sophie Rayworth, but no, he went for Red Rum.

"Come on love, you MUST see it, long face, fairly big nose, HUGE teeth, it's all there"

His teeth suddenly had just gained themselves a shorter life span as I pictured the shovel wiping that grin off his face – see – there's the murderous thing again! I digress, the teeth, yes, they had started to suddenly develop constant abscesses and were being removed at an alarming rate.

What the hell was going on? Was I to lose an arm next, or maybe just wait for my head to fall off? This was indeed a strange feeling.

All things were quiet on the co-parenting front with Mike, and the kids were well and truly settled in our new home and at the village school where the only one of us to get a bad report was me. So, why were all these strange things happening to my mind? Was I so settled and content that I was now indeed processing the truly painful and ugly divorce that I went through?

Was I finally coming to terms with what I had been through for all those years on my own with two tiny children, the tangible loneliness, the overwhelming sense of failure that I had not conformed to the norm as all my peers had? Why could I not just find peace and contentment? Would I always be plagued with what I had been put through?

Question after question consumed my addled brain and I realised I might need someone professional to talk to. When you go from having nothing, except your most valuable assets, your beautiful children, to having it all, shouldn't you be consumed by smugness? Overwhelming joy and a feeling of inner peace and relief? Well, I had no bloody idea what was going on, so I just kept buggering on and put one foot in front of the other and time passed with many more excruciating disasters on the horizon. But one in particular was the one that changed things for me. Changed them in a way that made me want to change them for ALL menopausal women.

It was a walk with Helen.

I like Helen.

Helen also has teenagers and is going through the menopause. Helen is also certifiable and as it turns out needs the same reconstructive surgery as me, as we both discovered when we got chatting about our menopausal plight. I always forget that Helen is a nurse so, how shall I put this, says it how it is. I was complaining about all my teeth gradually falling out when Helen, with no fucking warning at all, announced that her vagina fell out the other day... Now, this happened whilst I was in the middle of that large puddle of mud which some kindly person has put wooden planks over so that you can avoid getting sucked in by the foot deep quick mud that quickly engulfs you and swallows you whole.

Well, they hadn't quite factored in two middle aged women, one with an external vagina and the other with no pelvic floor who then proceeded to begin to laugh until the tears ran down her legs and then slipped spectacularly with one of the planks seemingly attached to one of my wellies, and considering that I am the only feckin wife in the village who hasn't been taken skiing this easter holiday, did a pretty feckin impressive parallel turn on one wooden plank and landed on my back in the freaking brown squelch. Far bloody cry from a breathtaking whoosh in Verbier!

The only bonus that came from this total mess was that the fact that I had definitely wet myself was totally disguised by the fact that I now looked like I had totally shat myself. But Helen and I were not perturbed. Oh no.

We are made of stern stuff, and besides, what more could do wrong now that we were off the beaten track and free to talk wildly and loudly of random urination and vaginal prolapses, oooh and we managed to sneak in a few tips on how to get out of sex with our husbands too. My suggestion of quietly mentioning yeast infections just as the beloved starts slipping off his pyjama bottoms was a bloody winner the other night. He totally overdid the gagging, but hey, whatever works. Helen liked it too, that's her kind o' lingo.

So we were merrily chatting away, about life, love, teenagers, smoking weed (the fact that we were going to start) when my fucking dog disappeared. Now, this can only ever mean one of two things: He's rolling in a huge pile of fox shit or he has found something dead to eat. We retraced our steps and sure enough, the fucker had got an entire skeleton and was doing a bloody good impersonation of a reckless forensic pathologist and was running around all over the field with this vile looking spinal column and skull in his mouth. Off I go again. Will I ever learn...

"Spencer! You feckin bastard dog, SIT SIT, oh you freaking bastard put that down!"

Spencer doesn't give a bloody hoot. Off he goes with me in hot pursuit.

"Come back here you shit bag, feckin bastard dog!"

I notice out of the corner of my eye that Helen has had to hit the ground. I think she is in fear that she may just lose her entire vagina completely if she stays standing up whilst watching this ridiculous spectacle. But I have to get this disgusting thing off my dog or he will eat the whole bloody lot and then need £30,000 worth of stomach surgery. So I continue with my chase. Helen is of no bloody use whatsoever, as she announces from her sitting position that she too has wet herself. Something has to give. I can't do this for much longer, literally every piece of my being is in some kind of motion.

Then it happens.

One stray bramble. That is all it took. Boot caught, Emma's upper torso and legs flung forward, wellies remain well and truly fixed to the ground and I perform an international quality accidental rugby tackle on Spencer and down the pair of us go. The silence that follows such an extraordinary vision is pretty magical until you realise that part of that silence is because Helen has not only lost the ability to stand up but has actually stopped breathing with pure hysteria.

The good news? I got the dead body off the dog. I, on the other hand, am covered in cuts, bruises, mud, pee and as it turns out, for posterity, a nice smear of cow shit. We both ended up sitting on a log, covered in just about every part of the spring countryside you could find, from mud, fox shit, blood from a dead carcass, a rather artistic swoosh from a fresh cow pat.

"What the hell is happening to me, Helen? I mean, I am sure I used to be a fairly bright, pretty average, uneventful sort of almost a 'flat coke' of a person – pretty unspectacular. Now look at me. I am a human tropical storm covered in shit! And the worst part of the whole scenario as I sit here with you now, is this feels like the norm to me these days."

Helen, who is still struggling a bit with my rather spectacular bringing down of my dog, did go silent and pensive for a while and then put her medical hat on.

"Honestly Em, I think you are well and truly in the midst of the menopause and you need help."

There it was. No frills. No sugar coating. The truth.

As we struggled our way back home, she had truly given me a lot of food for thought.

Although, so far, no one had actually been physically harmed in any of my extraordinary fiascos, they were becoming far more frequent and I was beginning to think that I was either heading for early onset Alzheimer's or worse, I had some kind of brain tumour that was making me make seriously odd decisions and many of my normal and reliable bodily functions were leaving the building.

This newly acquired incontinence was becoming a real issue. Could a brain tumour do that?

But there was no denying it now, I needed help and I needed an expert.

Chapter 19 - Becoming a human aircraft carrier

After much trawling through the internet and various parts of social media, I was recommended to see a private practitioner who came highly recommended and would put me right! She was going to sort all my craziness, mischief and lunacy! YEY! This was of course a total load of shite, but at least we might be able to get my anxiety and brain fog under control and hopefully find the part of my brain that I THINK I once had and reinstate and reboot it. So, with no further ado, off I went to see her.

Off I dragged my ever-increasing mass to this lovely lady who not only totally got it but had the answers! I had gained a delightful total (weight for it – get it?) 4 stone in the space of a matter of 2 years post-surgery and 3.9 stone of that was where my waist used to be! Google maps were a matter of days away from declaring me as a roundabout.

I remember, asking Ed if I had in fact gained any weight during the post op period and being a man of SOME intelligence, he was diplomatic when I asked him if I were to jump up and down in the middle of our bedroom should we time how long it took parts of me to actually stop moving after I had finished. His response,

"Could you perhaps do it at the edge of the room, love, I am a surveyor, there are ceilings at stake...."

Anyway, after bloods taken and glucose checked, it was confirmed that I was fully menopausal, not going completely bonkers and also borderline Type 2 diabetes. I was jubilant! Yep, did a little dance in her waiting room and then needed to be called back in as bordering on Type 2 diabetes was nothing to be celebrated apparently. I was just so relieved that I wasn't a nutter! (Sadly, as you read on, you will realise that that last statement is NOT strictly true). No, this needed fixing and fixing fast.

I was told that I was in fact, as many menopausal women are, insulin resistant.

I had no idea what this meant so she explained in Emma-terms (yes yes, she used crayons) that basically my body was flooding itself with insulin and it was not being used, other than to build a rather valiant and stoic wall of fat around my middle.

Well, blow me down, I had no idea insulin was a hormone let alone that it was capable of this amount of damage!

I had my wedding coming up and I did NOT want to walk down the aisle of the registry office looking like an aircraft carrier, so some news of a solution was hugely welcome! The aim, apparently, was to cut ALL sugar out of the diet. Easy peasy! I could go without chocolate for a few months, which was the time I had to lose 4 stone before the big day. Turns out, there are a few things that take you by surprise when your body goes through 'changes', in my case, that losing weight is not as simple as going on a crash diet and the weight dropping off over a matter of a week or so, like being 23 again. Oh no no no, this was in fact more like turning the Titanic. Brakes on, systems in reverse and then 6 weeks later a pound a week was dropped. Also, the whole "cut out sugar" was not quite as simple as stopping the cinema sized bags of minstrels every night, it was almost bloody everything, most of which wasn't even remotely sweet! Potatoes were banned, over cooked pasta, out the window, rice, history and as for bread – well that couldn't even be looked at!

To cut a very long story short, I did in fact go down the aisle the size of an aircraft carrier and have never been more grateful for flapper dresses that are essentially large sacks with a few sequins on them. Also, easy to wear with seriously ugly but very comfortable shoes. Yes, the day had finally come.

Wedding numero deux. Totally unplanned, totally disorganised and a small disaster all of its own. But it was also a day that I NEVER EVER in a million years thought I would see after catastrophe number 1. I took my first marriage extremely seriously, even though it was a bit of a non-event right from the start. I took my vows seriously, my responsibility seriously and marriage seriously.

I was also acutely aware that (a) my Dad had paid for it and would kill me if I fucked it up and (b) there was not ONE single divorce in my entire extended family!

So, when my first husband left the scene rather swiftly and with not much explanation, I was not only devastated but full of self-blame and shame too.

To the point that for many, many years I felt as if I was not worthy of anyone's love, let alone that kind of crazy commitment that is marriage. And yet, here I was, 10 years after my first divorce, standing with my beautiful girls, aged 11 and 12, me dressed as a sparkly warship, bracing myself for the day of our lives.

To be fair, I had been determined from the start of this wedding, to make it an extremely low-key affair. Second time around for us both and I knew I would make as shit a bride as I did the first time. The first time was spent mainly looking for my maid of honour's husband who went missing mid reception. We were deeply concerned that he had fallen in the Thames as he was a tad worse for wear but he had in fact passed out on bench in a faraway graveyard and my best friend and I carried him home and having to explain to my new husband why my wedding dress was covered in grass stains and soil as well was interesting to say the least. Anyway, the only things we ACTUALLY organised in the official sense of wedding planning was the music that we would walk into the registry office, sign the register to and leave the building to. We also organised a marquee and some caterers for the after party.

Firstly, it turned out that the CD player at the venue was buggered so we walked in together in total silence and a lot of sniggering – we have very childish family and friends – someone could have pointed out BEFORE I walked down the aisle that I had a large sticker on my bottom. And then after exchanging vows where neither of us could keep a straight face, we headed to the reception where Ed had extremely generously catered for the 100 people we had invited. What I had forgotten to tell him was that I had essentially been walking around the village for weeks in advance telling anyone and everyone that they MUST pop in for a sherbert or two. As we walked in as Mr and Mrs my new husband's first words to me were,

"Emma, who the feck are all these people?"

I breezed over it by making the most embarrassing speech of my life where I recounted tales of drunken skiing holidays and setting fire to the garden then flooding it. My mother-in-law never really liked me anyway.

Luckily for me our best man managed to accidentally distract us from the fact that we had about 200 people in the marquee and that the caterers were having small little nervous breakdowns. He did this in such a stylish and subtle way. He drank his way through ALL the wine at the wedding lunch and then, as he could not in fact stand once at the reception, he proceeded to greet people, on his hands and knees by praying and licking their shoes. He also prevented many relatives and guests from leaving by biting their socks. Genius. Pure genius.

I left our wedding 3 hours earlier than my brand-new husband for 2 reasons. I was absolutely crap at being the centre of attention and the people who were looking after Spencer declared that he had started to throw up everywhere so as the kids always come first, I scooped the girls up, went to get the chundering hound and once all three were settled I sat for a precious 2 hours in absolute peace on the sofa and closed my eyes. I did not sleep. Far from it.

I felt the tears of relief and joy pour down my face as I realised, I was no longer alone in this journey through life, and nor would I ever again. I had found my best friend in the world, my rock, my hope and we were forever betrothed to one another. As I sat there, so quietly and so still, I could actually see the colours of my life brighten a little.

The dark cloud that had settled over my psyche for so many years, the one that dulled the colour of life had gone and the radiance of hope was restored. What is totally moving about moments like this is they take you by surprise, for I had had no idea that the colours had indeed been tinted for so long, I had become so accustomed to their shade that when they were dusted off and polished, it was like a light had come on inside me and I don't think I will ever forget that moment for the rest of my life.

We honeymooned as all romantic couples do. With 5 kids, 3 large dogs in a beautifully converted mill in France. It was utter gin fuelled chaos and so much fun. Spencer and his counterparts saw off many a cyclist by chasing them and scaring the living crap out of them as they passed through Lucy's land and on both journeys there and back, he disgraced himself at just about every service station possible, even entered a public lavatory where I had left the door slightly open to be exposed, pants around me ankles, on the throne with Spencer at my side for all the French to see.

And so, life went on. In its usual chaotic style. Both the girls had begun at the local secondary school which could be likened to Grange Hill in the 21st century. It was quite a rollercoaster ride, and I had the Heads of House on speed dial which was always a joy.

Mike had in the meantime moved to the USA to pursue a career over there, heading back every month to see the kids and his new girlfriend, a lovely girl called Consuela, we called her Connie. She lived not too far from us so once again, we had struck gold, the kids adored her and her boys who were only a tad older than them but took them under their wing as big brothers and for a short while life was peaceful and quiet. We seemed to be over the worst.

Then it happened. I broke my mum's golden rule: never sit back and think,

"I've got this whole life thing licked. All is well, ducks in a row, sit back, relax, you got this".

It is like a conjuring trick for a small implosion.

The girls had had a fabulous time with Connie, her boys and their Dad up in London just before Christmas, we had all met up to do the handover halfway and Connie and Mike were heading over to his home country in Europe and we all wished each other a Merry Christmas and we headed off home for me to begin the annual turkey cremation.

Just before the New Year celebrations I got a call from Connie. I could hear it, again, that sound in someone's voice. Heartbreak, sorrow, loss.

"We've broken up, I don't know what to do".

"Oh my love, I am so so sorry, I don't know what to say, are you sure it isn't just the time of year a blip, too much pressure?"

I could hear myself almost pleading with her to make this right. She was like Chrissie, an amazing step mum and she was a huge comfort to me when the girls were away.

"It's a long story Em, but it's over, and I don't know what to do. But, the reason I am calling you is because I can't lose those beautiful girls of yours, they mean the world to me, PLEASE can we stay in touch?"

Honestly, my heart was broken for her. I knew how this felt but more importantly, BANG, there went step mum number 2 who adored my girls. I sat for a moment and gathered my thoughts; how bloody selfish can you actually be Emma? This girl's world and future has been shattered and all you can think about is your kids and your peace of mind. Having suitably chastised myself I realised that this was salvageable and, in more ways than one.

"Come down, come down now. The girls would love to see you and I can't bear the thought of you being alone."

"Are you serious? Really? Can I come and hug the girls?"

"Of course you can. They adore you and would hate to think that you were alone during this time. Heartbreak is the worst, and you would be pushing on the old proverbial open door with me so you are coming to a place of safety."

And she did, and from that gorgeous, warm, tearful, understanding 2 hours a lifelong friendship was born. An unlikely one, much like that of Chrissie and me, but finding solace in the people who you can share your pain with is unbelievably cathartic and I had been taught in life that if you CAN be kind to people, do it.

I had also tried to instil into the girls another vital value, and that was that relationships, ones that truly mean something, are NOT disposable, and from there I stood by that value and to this day, their relationships with both their stepmothers, sadly now 'ex' ones, are as solid as they were when they were such a huge part of their lives. My friendships with both of my successors are to this day often my safe place and we are as close as any girlfriends should be i.e. I have danced on a very smart pub table with them both and been caught as I fell off into a crowd of rather smart people from Battersea. A standard sign of a first class, long term friendship.

Chapter 20 - Life goes on

Mike went back to the US and life went on as normal. That is another story, one to be told by my children, not me. But the long shadow of divorce and co-parenting was once again cast over our family for a short while. But, as with all things in life, it's a case of pick yourself up, dust yourself off and move on. I stayed in close touch with Connie and she took great comfort in the return of her boys back into the fold and the love that she got back from her step daughters. She was going to be fine, as was Chrissie, they were empaths and had strong spirits, they too would survive this break up.

My life continued as life does. Mother, road safety officer, wife, housekeeper. One week ran into the next with very few disasters and I was beginning to think that this menopause lark was totally responsible for all my faux pas. Now that they had levelled out my HRT and the old Oestrogen levels were back to where they should be, I could start to venture out more, UNSUPERVISED!

I offered to pop down to Homebase to help my lovely husband who was definitely the DIY king around the house which he readily accepted. I mean, what could possibly go wrong?

All we needed were a couple of pots of paint and I was done. Out I pop, having made no noise or chaos in the store carrying my two pots of paint, two roller kits, paintbrushes, masking tape and a large bucket. Don't ask for a bag of course, I am a woman and can and will multi-task. So, on waddling towards my car dressed as a decorating packhorse I spy a small car whose handbrake has evidently been left off and is careering its way solo towards another parked car. Instantly I became Wonderwoman.

Paint tins discarded in a matter of milliseconds, paint everywhere, and I mean, everywhere. But this is of no importance, I am about to save several lives and a lot of damage to people's property. Heroine mode is well and truly engaged. Race to the front of the out of control Renault Clio and stand, legs apart with arms out in front of me (just as Linda Carter would have done) and throw my almighty weight onto the bonnet of the death trap that is this rapidly increasing in speed Renault.

Groaning and moaning with the strain, I finally bring the beast to a grinding halt. I slowly arise from my "over the bonnet" stance, and all the blood drains from my reddened face as I make rather surprising eye contact with a young and rather short young man in the driver's seat. He looks somewhat bewildered as he is faced with a middle-aged woman covered in "Mowforth White" emulsion crouched over the bonnet of his car.

"What the FUCK are you doing?"

Well, that's bloody gratitude for you! I nearly killed myself to stop his out of control vehicle, no handbrake, unmanned... *aaaaaahhhhhh...*

Penny slowly starts to drop.

Turns out he has a dicky battery and needs to bump start it in order to get anywhere and was seriously relieved when he managed to park on a bit of a hill in the DIY car park.
The silence was a good 20 minutes long when the ever-immortal words were shouted out of the driver's window.

"You can push me now you mad old woman!"

So much for being the superhero of the day! I have apologised a lot for a great deal of things in my life, but never more so I don't think about that moment. Perhaps supervision for a little while longer...

Chapter 21 - Life is never quite a clear picture is it?

So as life meandered along, often with days where absolutely nothing catastrophic happened and the seasons came and went, we hit that wonderful time of year where the sun came out (it's called the last few days before the summer holidays start) and one of the things that I have neglected to tell you is that we own a beach hut. I hear a little sharp intake of breath! It is indeed a mere shed on a beach with no electricity or running water, but it has saved me on so many occasions that I am deeply deeply in love with the little place. When my first marriage imploded and I found myself in that washing machine of life that I described earlier, I used to play a little mental game with myself. There was a barrier to get through in the car park and I would say to myself,

"Emma, your world of fear, alarm, uncertainty and battle are staying on THAT side of the barrier – they cannot come in here – this place is for peace, fun, relaxation and unadulterated, fabulous fun with my children."

And bugger me, it only worked! That little beach hut had and has a magical quality about it. You open the terrace doors, bring down the drawbridge and there she was in all her glory. Towels, boogie boards, a little kettle and a gas stove. Buckets, spades, paint to decorate the stones and even a curtain to hide yourself when you change!

The deck chairs would come out and Mum and I would sit down and just lean back and close our eyes and for a few brief minutes the world would stop. Time would literally stand still, and we had some semblance of true, in the moment, contentment. A true rarity these days. We always seem to be looking forward, planning, finding issues in the plans, changing the plans and then coming to terms with the plans and either dreading or being excited. Or equally looking back. Talking about what had happened the day before, the week before, a year ago or a past memory of a holiday or an incident.

How sadly uncommon it was to have those moments of just being and living IN THAT MOMENT and loving it.. Smiling through it. Just living it. That little beach hut, the simplest of things ever, gave me and my beautiful daughters that in abundance.

We all adored spending time there, just being with the sea and with my gorgeous Mum, laughing, enjoying stones, paddling in the freezing waves and somehow, although we often made time stand still, the days flew past far too fast because each minute was glorious and delicious and magical.

Those were truly our salad days and I honestly think that in so many ways, that gorgeous little hut and that crazy shingle beach saved us. It saved me. It brought me back down to earth and centred me. I was small. I had no real or meaningful control over anything. Was that the sea? Was that just being on the edge of something tangible? I sort of don't ever want to figure it out or understand it, I just know that it puts all my problems into perspective and anyway, they weren't there. They were waiting for me to be collected on the other side of that barrier.

With all that said, I am not for one moment saying these days were all straightforward and blissful, but the bits that were, were priceless. Because, for the past few years, well we took along a problem. One we did NOT leave behind that barrier. In fact, we took along two problems. One was 40kgs, yellow and Labrador shaped, the other was ME. Neither of us had been properly trained and we were a sight to behold when things went, how shall I put it, awry.

I discovered on one particular day, as I attempted to maintain some level of decorum at the beach with the ASBO dog, that some weight loss over the past 6 months would have been a prime idea.
This 49 year old body, which had been put through its "gin paces" got its first exposure to the outside world. And it wasn't looking so good let me tell you. It is SO true that not only white fat looks much worse than brown fat, but fat that has basically got a mortgage, a full-on contract and been resident on your body all winter, is not only like something off a bad Holby City scene, but bugger me once that blubber gets moving there is NO stopping it! Spencer of course took his first dip (accidently) and then produced one of his Jurassic sized shits bang smack in the middle of the beach. He then proceeded to do a lap of honour which involved flat out galloping, wiping out a couple of really really nice older people, spraying sand and pebbles everywhere, children screaming and then he finishes off by having a good old roll in the shingle. I am screaming at the feckin useless teenagers (my children)

"Get a bloody poop bag, NOW!"

They can't stop laughing.
So, I start my hunt.

My turd hunt.

Oh the glamour.

His turds may be massive, but they are like commandos on that bloody beach. Totally invisible. Now, can I just give you some perspective here re-my embarrassment. I am in a bikini. There are bits of me that are STILL moving from my first pursuit of the fucking dog, I have a Sainsbury's bag and no glasses and am looking frantically, under full supervision by the entire beach for a monster shit.

People started chiming in

"Warmer... oooh no colder, ooooooh yes warmer... eeeeoooooooow HOT"

Shit eventually not recovered but trodden in with one flip flop remaining and of course the barefooted victim. Quite a lot of dry heaving took place. Always a classy sight. It was only then that I looked up and to my horror I saw that the bastard dog had spotted a child with an ice cream. Oh dear God, I have one foot covered in dog shit, I am a flip flop down, we have a shingle beach and a potentially disastrous situation imminent. I know how this ends. Or at least I THINK I do.

Spencer begins his pursuit like a thoroughbred out of the gates. But either this kid was seriously savvy or had owned a lab before let me tell you, because he bolted that ice-cream down pretty damn pronto. This would have been a genius move had he not just turned himself into a human baby wipe covered in ice-cream. Oh shit fuck bollocks. I can see another £15,000 trip to the vet to wrench this from the dog's stomach. But I was NOT doing another visit the vet this month, so off I went again, Usain Bolt would have been proud of my sprint start, and like a highly tuned athlete in a fatsuit I finally caught up with the bastard hound and in front of the entire family I shoved my hand right down his throat and I pulled that chocolate covered baby wipe which was past his windpipe and on its way to labrador oblivion.

There were three seconds of silence as I looked on at my achievement, in hindsight, my celebratory scream of triumph and the bollocking I was just about to give Spencer was possibly unnecessary

"Oh yes! Oh yes! I got you little..."

STOP. Emma. Stop. Small children, lovely family, having a picnic. You are white, fat, still in motion and you have just retrieved a piece of their property from your dog's gullet by losing most of your hand and wrist for a good 10 seconds . And you. are. still. on. their. feckin. blanket.

"I am so sorry, but well done little man, excellent speed ice cream eating. Huge admiration. Good on ya..."

I drifted away from their tranquil scene with a belt around my bastard dog's neck to a ripple of giggling from the rest of the beach. You see, this is a really family orientated spot. Many come and stay and for Spencer and me, this means we are relatively well known. He has eaten entire bucket loads of fishermen's bait, stolen sausages of screaming hot barbecues and has even taken an entire pizza off two teenage lads – a 15 incher! That was an expensive day out. So, normally when we arrive, it is either just a general announcement that Spencer the ASBO dog is "in the hood" or if there are newcomers, a walk around with a blanket apology for lunchtime antics, an exchange of names so that I can be summoned at any time if Spencer approaches any picnic. Spencer loves the beach hut. He lies on the deck as if he owns the bloody place and checks out the size of people's cool boxes as they pass, and I swear to god, he checks out who he is going to pilfer first. On one particular occasion, I arrived there, and Mum had a friend there with their children. They had rather foolishly left their bag at the entrance to the hut and within minutes of our arrival spent greeting these old friends, it was noted that their packed lunch which consisted of a variety of bread rolls in a sealed food bag was missing...

Spencer?

No surely not. Too quick and he's funny about plastic. But we searched and searched and no shredded plastic or rolls were to be found. I knew I couldn't take the chance so about a turn, dog in tow, 45 minute drive to our local vets where his stomach was pumped immediately and a perfectly formed, totally unchanged, perfect bag of lunch rolls were produced by my revolting dog. The vet even said,

"We can just give them a rinse down and you can take them back if you like – basically untouched by stomach juices."

The dog is a legend. He is also a royal pain in the arse and has got me into numerous scrapes which no doubt you will hear more of as this ridiculous book goes on – let's hope this meno memory doesn't let me down!

Chapter 22 - We're all going on a summer holiday

The summers came and went, some spent at the beach hut, some spent on blissful Greek Islands with friends that were fellow Greek-o-files. Life was good. It was calm and it was easy.

It was during those summers that I would spend my time reflecting on what could have been. How the girls' and my lives could have turned out. The divorce was ugly and hard fought and if it hadn't been for the generosity of my Dad who paid for a good solicitor, we would have had nothing. Then, of course, came our wonderful Eddie who took the baton from my Dad and changed our lives forever. He took on my girls as his own and we were a family. His son stayed in touch with his Dad and our three children who were rather different in ages, were siblings almost straight away. I kept thinking that had I been able to see a 5 second glimpse of this life when I was back in that dark place, all those years ago, I would not have been so afraid.

Would we want a life like that? Without darkness? Without uncertainty? Without the fear of the unknown? Would that not take away the unadulterated joy of safety and stability? It's hard to know. But as I have always been told and I have learned to be the truth, nothing ever stays the same and uncertainty IS indeed always around the next corner, which is why those moments of pure joy, where the world stands still for you, just for a moment. I close my eyes, I take in the biggest breath and try and hold that feeling within me and try and find a place to store it, to wrap it up with a great big ribbon so I can find it when I need it, on those dark dark days when life delivers its inevitable pile of crap on you from time to time. It was one of the most valuable lessons my darling mum taught me, and I will take it to the grave.

I never believed that we would ever have such wonderful foreign holidays. When my world fell apart and I was thrust overnight into single motherhood, it was the last thing on my mind.

There was absolutely no way I would be able to afford delicious Greek island week escapes, no, that would be other's memories and stories to be watched in envy on Facebook and social media.

One year, in my single-I-can-do-this-days we were offered a wonderful chance of a beautiful house in Spain by some fabulous friends. My darling parents helped pay for the flights and despite worrying about my health at the time, I snapped up the offer. But it was terrifying! I flew, with two little tikes, aged about 5 and 6 to Seville where I had a 2 hour car journey to this beautiful hilltop town near in Andalucia where I was met by these fantastic friends of ours who were nearing the end of their stay and would only be with me for 2 nights. It was such a charming little place where not one fecker spoke a word of English!

Normally, this would thrill me as from memories of my twenties when visiting various spots on the Spanish coast, you were lucky to find any Spanish food let alone a Spaniard! My friends eventually left me unsupervised with two small children and a grumbling appendix in this strange yet wonderful place. We explored the area, mainly with my heart in my mouth as driving on the other side of the road did NOT exactly come naturally to me. My only two consolations were that I had tried to learn a little Spanish before leaving, but with my menopausal memory I had forgotten 80% of it. It's amazing how international sign language becomes when you need wine or 2 ice creams though. The other was that my darling Mum had agreed to join us after about 4 days on my own with the girls.

My biggest fear was that I would have another bout of appendicitis whilst in this strange place where no-one spoke an English and the girls would be looked after by some random stranger or even perhaps social services if I was rushed into hospital for the third time in as many months. But, we made it, and all we had to do was find our way back from Vejer to Seville airport and collect my gorgeous Mum who would be our new holiday companion for the remaining few days.

Ian had given me the most detailed directions to the airport and Karen, good bless her, had deliberately forgotten her DS which was shared in the car by the girls.
By some small miracle, I didn't miss that obscure turn off and ended up in bloody Madrid and found myself with the airport in sight and a load of Spanish road signs that I could not make head nor tail of. Which fecker was "Arrivals"???

By some small miracle, like a magical apparition, there was a Spanish policeman on a motorbike sitting in a lay-by. Now I knew this wasn't going to be straightforward as I couldn't speak a word of Spanish by now, the whole bloody lot had departed my brain and I doubted very much that he could speak English, but I needed to, so I pulled over.
I rolled down the window and managed the basics

"Buenos noches señor" (Goodnight sir – it was 11 am in the morning)

"Um, looking for arrivals, mama..."

Ok, sign language and a bit of acting it was.

I quickly turned myself into a human Boeing 737 and arms out, making engine noises. I did my best impersonation of a plane landing. The policeman tipped his head to one side. Ok, so I hadn't quite done the trick.

"Ok, so, Mama….." more acting as a landing plane, even doing the hand motion of the landing.

"Me" points at myself. Starts using the steering wheel as if I am bloody Mr Bean or a cartoon character to show that I am picking her up. Then try and do a 'question' action. Then I remember the words for "where"

"Dónde está señor"

The girls are in the back totally bemused by this interaction.
Then slowly but surely, a reassuring smile comes to the policeman's face and with a clear as day Liverpudlian accent he says,

"Are you looking for arrivals, love?"

Oh lord above, swallow me up whole NOW.

"You're English?"

"Yep, Liverpool born and bred, and may I say you have made my day – you really should be a pilot landing a plane like that, the sound effects were bang on."

Oh holy mother of God, I did the shushing noises and everything. I probably should have knocked his block off but being offered a police escort into the actual airport was too good an offer to pass up so bless him (the fucker) we followed him in and he even helped me to park, walked me in and there, in all her glory was my darling Mum. She did look a little perturbed as the girls and I stood there with a 6 ft 3" policeman but all was explained with great amusement between the two of them as I stood mortified.

But she was with us. I was no longer alone and no matter what happened then, I was safe.

So, that was not exactly the most relaxing holiday, but we got to see a parade of Andalusian horses and ate crepes with cream on until they came out of our ears and the four of us spent the final 3 days lapping up what I thought would be possibly the last foreign holiday we would ever have. Never underestimate the plight of single parents. Being alone is not the end of the world, but there are SO many occasions where the loneliness is tangible and you can almost taste it, especially on holidays. Seeing other families together and partners laughing and enjoying, if nothing else, the sanctuary of company, can be agony and used to reduce me to private tears at the end of a day spent with my little girls.

Just a note to you all who have taken the time to get this far through this ridiculous diary, memoir, book, whatever this is, if ever you see a single parent on a holiday. Seek them out. Invite them to join you for a drink. Sit and have a natter with them at the side of the pool. You may well be the only adult they have a conversation with the whole time they are on their hard earned holidays.

Trust me, it means the world. Anyway, Mum, the girls and I bid our farewell to Spain and the bittersweet holiday that the girls had loved – even the moment when their mother turned into a human flight and made friends with an enormous policeman called Keith!

And as luck would have it, I DID indeed have my final bout of appendicitis a matter of days after we arrived home and the bastard organ was removed so no more scares in that department. It was one of many times that luck, and timing were indeed on my side.

But, thanks to the luck and timing of that school reunion and the entry of Eddie into our lives who not only married this nutter, but became the best step father EVER to our two little girls, we DID get to live the dream. Foreign holidays with the shelter and security of an actual responsible adult with me who took control and did not find the need to spread his arms and become a charter flight just to collect someone from an airport...

However, there was one small issue with these Greek Island holidays which meant things weren't quite as smooth as they could have been – that would be ME. May I also add, that we were well and truly settled into our marriage at this point and could have the odd spat here and there. In fact, suffice it to say, we had also got what I believe they call 'the first few days of the holiday murder moments.'

Somehow or another, I would always let the clientele of the hotel know that the clampetts had indeed arrived much to Ed's embarrassment and on this particular holiday I was once again not going to disappoint. First day of holiday in Crete. Mark well and truly made. The beloved discovered last night that there were quite a few of the ol' Sunbed baggers in situ, so he got up very early this morning with our newly acquired towels and claimed what he thought were the best sunbeds around the pool.

Of course, he was totally wrong and had managed to get the only four sunbeds that were completely bang in the middle of the Sun and no shade whatsoever. The annual, but compulsory first day holiday row occurs in front of many interested onlookers. But being British twats that we are, it was all pretty silent and just mouthed swear words, insults and looks of death.

But nobody was stupid they all knew the drill: we were about to kill each other.

Anyway, to cut a long story short the fecker wasn't budging so I took it upon myself to move one of those enormous umbrellas over to the sunbeds in order to provide the shade that my pasty white family desperately needed.

That was quite a sight to behold because shit bag husband refused to help me because I had called him and unmentionable name and had in fact forgotten to just 'mime' it and the whole audience was instantly aware that the beloved was indeed a "stubborn, small man syndrome wankpuffin."

I digress.

It is quite surprising how much noise a 51-year-old woman in a tankini dragging a large parasol held down by about 50 kg of concrete can make. I think the sound of scraping across the concrete was possibly the most excruciating. For all of us bar one. Oh yes, the husband was properly starting to enjoy his hols and his wife's stubborn ridiculousness.
Finally got the bastard umbrella in between our sunbeds, totally drenched in sweat, which was extremely attractive to all my new audience, I then tried and erect said parasol to only find myself completely trapped inside it. For a few moments, I had time to think. What to do? There was NO way at this stage of the proceedings that I was going to give my husband the satisfaction of my epic failure but I was becoming acutely aware of two things: one being that there was the distinct possibility that I was going to collapse from heat exhaustion having wrestled with this bastard umbrella and was now basically a part of it and the temperature was rising by the minute, but also I had been standing, inside the closed piece of furniture, with just my legs sticking out for a good 4 minutes by then and must be looking rather odd.

Oh sod it, I needed help and my bloody husband knew it.

Apparently, according to the kids, all you could hear to begin with were muffled sounds of cries of help to an increasing crescendo of-

"Will you get me out of here you feckin twat! I can't fucking breathe."

There was quite a lot of laughter, which I assumed was from my family but when I was finally released from my parasol prison, it turned out that a fairly large crowd of the people around the pool who had come to assist but had been told to back away by my husband were actually hysterical with laughter.

Emma had arrived. Mortified.

After a few hours baking like a potato, starting to resemble one, but far too afraid to move in case I drew MORE attention to myself, I plucked up the courage and decided to have a quick dip in the pool before heading up to the room for a bit of much needed shade. Now, this was not going to be simple or elegant, we all know that.

Did I fall in? I did not.

Did I belly flop? Sorry nope.

What I did however was, after my extremely elegant breaststroke across the pool, was to climb the little ladder that is not designed at all for women of a certain age with enormous tankini bottoms that just happened to be no longer in place. Sort of thigh range I would say. So, enormous white arse on full display to my newfound audience. The joy of it all?

Did I notice? Did I buggery?

My departure from the pool area was watched closely by many of our fellow holiday makers who evidently assume I'm a new addition to the bloody entertainment team.

Oh Christ on a bike, get me out of here.

Head down, flip flops hurriedly put on the wrong feet, stumbled like a large sea mammal with my towel, my book and desperately trying to hold my pants up, straight up to our room. Slipping over in the reception was a breeze as only one receptionist was there and was terribly kind as she pulled me up from the floor and assured me that this happened frequently.
And you would think that the story would be over.

Wouldn't you?

Alas no, for this is me. Dingbat deluxe.

Get into room, remove totally fucking useless tankini, hang the drenched wretched thing over the balcony. Forget that the top half, which has quite an engineering job to do keeping my ever-enlarging breasts in place, was also removed and hung on the rail. But it was wet and therefore very heavy, and without any warning it slipped slowly and agonisingly off the balcony and fell to its death onto the balcony below.

Oh FFS!

Another visit to a kind lady at reception to ask to be let into the room below to retrieve my over shoulder boulder holder. But, before that, I look down and my problem is even larger than my white arse AND my menopausal breasts put together. For there, below me, was a bald man having his lunch peacefully on HIS balcony, who got the fright of his life as my enormous bikini top up landed perfectly, draped like a pair of rabbit ears on his head.

Emma's menopausal brain to mouth filter enters the moment.

"Oh my word, I'm so sorry" would have sufficed, but no, not me. Why not make a TOTAL fool of oneself when the opportunity arises?

So completely topless, everything that has seen better days on show, I chose:

"Shit shit bollocks, are you ok???"

He slowly removed his new sodden headwear and looked up. The sight he was confronted with must have been utterly terrifying, two enormous white bean bags, a well-developed and nurtured roll of fat below it and a towel desperately trying to escape from its place almost revealing a totally naked middle aged woman.

As luck would have it, he was a very nice man with an excellent sense of humour who I met on the stairwell to hand me back my clothing, with tears running down his face.

I'd say about 70 odd.

Apparently, he hadn't laughed that much since his wife left him in 1994.

Of course, the embarrassment didn't end there, oh no. You would think that a few lessons over the years would have been learned, but alas no, this is me. You see when you are such a natural clutterfuck such as myself, you get careless, forgetful of all the things that can and, in my world, DO go wrong. Case in point, I had got far too relaxed around the pool area and was often to be found sitting at the edge of the turquoise pool momentarily enjoying the peace and tranquillity of this glorious place, imagining that I had a look of Ursula Andress about me as I sat there, gleaming with Ambre Solaire, stomach sucked in, only to be the subject of another glorious family joke –

"Whose turn is it to push mum in?"

When you are basically 70 odd kilogrammes of loveliness you do not enter the water smoothly or elegantly, no no no, when pushed you are like a small tsunami covering half the other sunbathers around the pool. I spent so many of those holidays apologising for my family and me, but mainly for me as I cannot blame my family for one of the lessons that I never ever did learn: that there is in fact no elegant way to mount a lilo as a 51 year old woman.

On this particular holiday, after several attempts at doing it from within the pool I decided that I would do what I used to do as a teenager. Spot my first school girl error? What should have been at the forefront of my mind was a lesson that I swore I would never forget when I attempted to do a cartwheel in the pub garden. It turns out that you CAN in fact forget how to do those.

Anyway, as per usual, I did not learn that lesson. Instead, I lined the lilo up and then took a running jump and with all my might, and imagined skill, I tried aiming to land squarely on the lilo which was supposed to then skim, with me on it, across the water like an elegant swan. Of course this didn't happen as I had just recently applied a lot of suntan oil, resulting in me landing on the lilo, sliding straight off the front of it and ended up with the pillow jammed between my thighs which rendered my enormous backside pointing in the air along with the back of the lilo which did the same thing and we basically recreated an incredibly unattractive version of The Titanic.

I finally emerged from my position as a large ship, hair all over my face to the well deserved round of applause from all our fellow holiday makers. I think they were all rather looking forward to my "next trick" when I had actually hit the alcohol! How my children survived the embarrassment of their mother over these years, I will never know, but I think it has taught them well that making a total twat of yourself and then owning it, is no bad thing and I have tried to get around it often by saying

"It's much better to be a walking disaster than dull".

This sadly only REALLY washes when they are under the age of 12. As soon as the teenage years kick in, you are toast!

Chapter 23 - My Mum

Now, I hope by the time you have reached this stage of this mad little menopausal mayhem mother memoir, you have realised that from a really dark and scary time of your life, you can in fact emerge – albeit a little bruised and battered and with your reputation in tatters – vaguely triumphant. The lights do come on again, the colours do become brighter, and life DOES get better.

There is one person in particular who hasn't featured enough at this point, but there is a good reason for that. Because without her, I would quite simply NOT have made it this far and most certainly would NOT have had so much fun along the way. Everyone needs a guiding light. That doesn't necessarily have to be a person. It can be faith, or self belief, inner strength or just a guiding memory that never leaves you. I was eternally blessed with a wonderful circle of friends who held my hand through so many of my darkest hours. My best friend in the world, my darling Nicholotis (not her real name – a nickname from the age of 5) who never left my side for one moment and guided me through every emotion I went through when Mike left and helped me with some amazing, seriously sound advice about how to handle co-parenting and when the loneliness became too much, well, she would drop everything and be there. She was not the only one. There are truly too many to mention, but they know who they are.

But my guiding light, my rock in that sea of chaos, was the lady who made me. The lady who taught me every life lesson I would ever need to not only survive but to thrive.

My Mum.

I am dedicating this chapter to the most amazing woman who has ever walked this planet and honoured us all with her presence.

My mum taught me how to BE a mum.

I was loved from day one to within an inch of my life. I was made to feel like her sunshine and world, and I knew that no matter what, my life was safe in her hands and no matter what happened to me, she would let me find my own way until she could see I was floundering, and then ever ever so gently, she would guide me back, hold my hand and lead me to a safe place. Her love.

ALL my childhood memories are happy ones. Well, I say ALL. I was royally humiliated when I was 9 and we were taken to France on a family holiday, given 10 francs and told we could buy whatever we wanted in this little souvenir shop. I was given strict instructions by my mum that that did NOT include some ghastly earrings. So, what did I buy? Yes, you've got it. She rarely lost her temper with us as kids, but that day, I saw the boundary of my mum's tolerance and I never went to that place again.

Mum was rarely sensible at times when she should have been. Something that I adored about her and was so unique and endearing about her. My Dad, who was working his way up the career ladder in the oil industry, definitely needed a sensible and serious wife. Thankfully for us all, him included, he got the opposite. He took her on two "overseas" work trips, one to Malta and one to the US. Easily bored with "work chat" Dad was often found asking the question of his fellow work colleagues, "Has anyone seen my wife?"

In Malta, they were attending a smart drinks party for the oil industry and on asking this soon to become infamous question someone said,

"Isn't that her?"

A lady in cocktail dress was seen water skiing past.

Yes, it was my mum, who had got bored and then walked to the end of the jetty, got chatting to some Maltese chaps who asked her if she fancied a 'quick whizz around the harbour behind their speed boat' which my mum immediately agreed to. Dad and his fellow colleagues all watched on suddenly as my mother disappeared around the peninsula and was gone for a good 15 minutes. Thinking she had been kidnapped, they all got themselves in a little panic until she safely reappeared, looking windswept and interesting and a tad salty, deftly hopped off the boat, said her thank you's and reappeared at the dull drinks party as if nothing had happened.

Her next debacle was in the US of A – Dallas, I think. Another drinks party that bored the living crap out of mum. Dad, once again uttered the immortal words,

"Has anyone seen my wife?"
This time the answer was a little more straightforward.

"That's her up there surely?"

And surely it was. For there was my mum standing on the stage of this incredibly plush and formal room, dressed in full regalia as the statue of liberty with an ice cream as her torch.
This time she looked a little more uncomfortable as she had been chastised, I believe for the previous genius behaviour, but had apparently been commandeered to perform as Lady Liberty by one of the entertainment staff.

Dad was obviously mortified, and this was, I believe, the last time he took her away on a foreign business trip in order to prevent any more damage to his ever blossoming career. Her excellent behaviour did not end there though as she attended an extremely smart wedding with my Dad and he uttered, for the final time, the deadly phrase to someone rather posh,

"I don't suppose you have seen my wife?"

Only to be led out of the marquee to find my mother on the roof with a load of ushers sliding down the large tent having a bloody wail of a time. To my father's horror, she made it into the local paper! These are just a few stories of my darling Mum. In reality she was so much more than this, so much more than someone who was afraid of nothing and was never concerned with *Keeping up with The Joneses* – she was the most extraordinary person I have ever known.

She taught me that giving people your time was infinitely more important than giving them money or stuff. She sort of hated "stuff" – if she had stuff, she had invariably made it herself. I was only a disappointment to my mum in a couple of areas.

I was a child of the disposable era and had about as much ability for craft as a hairbrush. I also hated shopping. She would have loved a charity shopping partner; I was not that person. She had time for everybody and more energy than anyone I have ever known. She could do almost anything. From upholstery to picture framing, making clothes to being one of the best and most dedicated gardeners I have ever known.

She was a catastrophic cook who once invited some rather important people round for lunch and thought she would impress them with her imaginary culinary skills by stuffing the chicken with rosemary. She was evidently distracted whilst picking the rosemary from her immaculate garden and stuffed it with lavender, so the rather smart lunch guests were treated to cremated roast potatoes, home grown chard and chicken that tasted like it had spent the day at a spa and tasted of soap. Another culinary triumph.

There were many Christmases where the turkey was a figurehead of the day for all the wrong reasons. She once decided to try and cook it slowly in the bottom aga overnight and serve it up all "falling off the bone and succulent" (these were her words as she pulled the stone cold, totally uncooked bird from the oven an hour before serving time) – tragically, my father had warned her that this would not work, but never one to be perturbed or indeed to listen to my Dad, she went into a mild state of panic and grabbed my brother and I to save the day by chopping the bastard thing up and microwaving it. It was NOT the royal success she would have liked but Bernard Matthews would have had a field day with what we were made to eat that Christmas. Mind you, nothing that several bottles of Dad's finest Cabernet Sauvignon couldn't hide.

My Mum was all about family. We were and still are a large family who were always at the centre of her world. But family was never just about blood to her. She had a vast array of friends who she saw as her family and both my brother and I were brought up surrounded by people who loved us all, especially my Mum. We were taught from an early age that people were far more important than money or things. Her message to me, which I have tried to hand on to my girls, is that when you are feeling low or scared at any stage of your life, the best therapy ever is to reach out to someone or more than one person and help THEM.

I do believe that my Mum is a HUGE factor in the blog page that I write on social media that ended up with a quarter of a million followers. When I was at my lowest ebb. When I felt like an epic failure in life, I chose to share that rather than hide it away and pretend. She taught me to be real and I listened. It breaks my heart, that as I sit here and write this, I am writing about this amazing lady in the past tense.

She fought cancer three times in her life. First, when I had just married my first husband with Stage 4 breast cancer, there was no stage 5. She kicked that fucker into touch, after 6 months of the most gruelling and devastating chemotherapy and a double mastectomy. 5 years later she had the unbelievable bad luck to contract a totally unrelated throat tumour… BUT, she was not ready to go yet and by some miracle it was small and treatable with once again some horrific radiotherapy which made her throat close up and paralysed her vocal chords. She was told that she may never speak again – no chance! With the news of having 5 years to live, she carried on as only my Mum would, giving her time and energy to others and she swanned past her 5 year curfew until a few months ago, after 13 years, it came for her.

This time with such a vile vengeance it was utterly heartbreaking to watch. It took everything that she loved from her. She would never eat again. She would never drink again and she would never talk again. We could only sit and watch as this remarkable soul, this force of nature, this absolute one off was eaten alive by this devastating disease. But, despite her suffering hourly, she STILL found the strength to smile and be interested in others.

In fact, her last text message she ever sent was to a friend to see how SHE was. Her and my Dad were in love for 57 years, married for 54. I still get phone calls from her friends who can't believe she is gone who are grieving as much as I am. Thankfully, Dad, my brother and I could be with her in her final days where she gave us the gift of 3 hours of wakefulness during her long periods of unconsciousness so we could say our goodbyes and our thank yous.

I am the woman I am today because of her. In so many ways, I am her and those elements of me I am most proud of. Every fall, every bit of mischief, every break of every rule was from her and she lives on in me forever.

Chapter 24 - Blending families and feckin chaos

So, with the kids turning rather too quickly into teenagers and me most definitely NOT prepared for 3 hormonal women in the house. We bought a new one. One with a man cave in the garden that was fiercely fought over by Eddie and me. I finally saw sense and realised that if I wanted my marriage to last, he needed it far more than I did! Parents evenings at secondary school were always a joy. Long gone were permission slips and making papiermaché castles, this was MY chance to shine and embarrass my children in yet another way – making friends with their teachers and creating more eye rolling and shin kicking. Suffice it to say, I made a mark whenever I entered that building, and the girls never quite came out unscathed or indeed talking to me.

I seemed to become a popular mum amongst their friends however, with my absolute inability to actually grow up myself and joining in their scattered gatherings with my Rick Mayall-esque dance routines after a few glasses of dutch courage. Sadly, or fortunately for my beautiful daughters, I was never going to be a conventional 'sensible' Mum but an endless source of embarrassment and hideous head in hand moments. When I envisaged parenting teenage girls, I thought the words,

"Move on" would be used by me to encourage them to get over heartbreak on fallings out with girlfriends, it's sort of ended up with them begging me, with a rather firm hand in the small of my back at various school occasions to

"Move on" and "let's get the feck out of here before you open your mouth any further to embarrass us."

Plans eh?

I am trying to think about when the embarrassments truly started from the kids' perspectives. I made the immortal and unrepeatable mistake of actually asking my youngest daughter. She began with a few dashes between hospitals because I had had a bit of an accident in my running days.

In short, I was jogging – I can't bring myself to call it running because elderly people often strolled past me, I was going so slowly – and I basically fell over the bloody dog who decided to stop directly in front of me and a totally inelegant swallow dive onto some unwelcoming black gravel of a disused railway track ensued. I am not going to deny it, nor be ashamed of it, but I cried. In fact, I wailed like a toddler does as they run and splat face first onto the pavement. I rang Eddie who was instantly alarmed as the track was remote and from my breathless and panicked sobbing, he assumed I had been attacked, or worse.

"Em, EM, EMMMMM, calm down love, what on earth has happened??? Are you ok?"

The kids had overheard his alarm and had quickly gathered around him to check that their mother was not in A & E after some horrible incident.

"Em, calm down, breathe, love, are you ok, good god, what's happened you are seriously scaring me"

Long silence. I gather myself.

Sobbing into the phone I manage :

"I've fallen over..."

You can actually hear the -

"Oh for fucks sake, she's bloody fallen over AGAIN!"

FROM. THEM. ALL.

In fairness they did all jump in the car to come and collect their injured mother and her arch enemy the bastard Spencer who is definitely trying to kill me. The driver because he knew that my knee was incapable of actually getting me home and the other two to see how much blood there was and have a good laugh at their mother's expense.
I needed stitches in my elbow and a plaster on the graze on my knee. I had slightly overreacted as it turns out, but it was bloody painful!

So littlun comes with me for the stitches. Wrong hospital the first time. Second time, 2 hours wait and only two stitches required. All a bit of a palaver really. I decided the only way forward was to hit the pub and anaesthetise myself.

"Do you remember, Mum, when you had your big op and you came into our Year 6 classroom with your trousers on inside out?"

"Well yes, but surely that didn't affect anyone too personally?"

"The reality is, Mum, no, they were used to it, you had done it several times before."

"Ah."

"So what was the problem then?"

"Well I had told them that you had been in hospital having a hysterectomy but none of us really knew what that meant, so when you came in, Jake put his hand up and asked you what you had had done."

"And?"

"Mum, you told him that you had basically been spayed. No-one talked to me for a week".

Ok, I can see how that could be tricky.

Then she continued.

"Do you remember that Friday evening at the pub with the dog?"

Getting mildly panicked here, I realised that there were quite a few Fridays to choose from.

"Would that be the one when Spencer ate a live rabbit in front of everyone having their dinner and I managed to pull its back legs out, tried to luzz it over the fence, slightly miscalculated my underarm throw and it ended up actually flying behind me?"

"Oh yes, there was that one, but this one was better, it was the one where you took back 7 kids and tried to turn the spare room into a massive sleepover den by taking all the mattresses off all the beds and trying to fit them all in the spare room."

"You were struggling with getting two of them to lie down flat so you tried bouncing on them with what you kept describing as your "sizeable arse" but it wouldn't go flat so you started yelling for me to come and help you."

"So? I was being a great Mum, loads of kids, bit too much vino but hey, you were having a great time"

"Well not really."

"Why?"

"We were all a bit frightened"

"What on earth were you frightened of?!"

"You were bouncing quite high at one point, Mum, and I was actually under the mattress..."

Ah.

"Oh yes, then there was the time that you had your birthday at the pub..."

Oh holy mother of god, what the feck did I do to my poor daughter this time?

"You and your friends had a lovely time apparently, or so you told me the next morning as we were walking to school..."

It was then that it started coming back to me. Oh, dear lord, the new vicar, the new school vicar, SHIT SHIT SHIT.

He had joined the parish of our village with a rather strange but, all the same, sweet ritual of praying on the corner of the main drag on a Thursday.

This was his FIRST Thursday.

My birthday at the pub was the Wednesday night before.

A lovely time had been had by my lovely village mates and I had been spoiled rotten with some lovely gifts.

A little too much wine had been consumed and Paula and I had started our rather "curvy" journey home which seemed to be taking much longer than anticipated as we were covering rather more mileage due to a distinct lack of balance or direction. I put this down to me carrying all the wrapping paper from the presents that I had been so luckily lavished with that night, so disposed of those in the bin on that fateful corner.

I finally made my way home and fell like a tree onto my side of the bed with Eddie having to remove my footwear and my standard 'jeans and a nice top' – every girls' staple outfit for a night out.

On awakening, I opened one eye to ensure I was in fact still (a) still alive and (b) home and not actually under a neighbour's hedge – both having been confirmed I then bravely opened the other eye and BAM! There it was, the hangover to end all hangovers. Oh, FFS Emma, when will you ever learn??? Still, be grateful for one thing, you did not make a fool of yourself in the pub and you had a lovely time and would get to thank all your gorgeous friends in the playground for your special birthday gifts.

So, first things first. What were the bloody gifts and who gave you what? I headed downstairs rather gingerly as descending the staircase on my arse was just NOT an option this morning. Went straight for the bag of gifts that I had carefully gathered up at the end of the evening and separated from the wrapping paper. Quite unlike me as it happens, but, hey, everyone has to grow up eventually heh?

Turns out this was not that time for me as I started rummaging through the bag and slowly and extremely painfully it was beginning to dawn on me that I had actually kept all the wrapping paper and had in actual fact thrown all the presents in the bin... Oh shit fuck bollocks.

I gathered myself as I had a school run to perform and could in fact very discreetly rummage around in the bin for the presents and do a sort of drug deal type swap on the quiet.

Jaime would just have to live with it and I could come up with some kind of reason that I was disposing of the rubbish from the night before and then found a bag of someone else's stuff. Blagging my way through this morning was definitely the way forward.

What I had NOT factored into the whole equation was the vicar. The new vicar. Him and his Church of England ritual of praying for a village once a week in his full vicar regalia just happened to be on that very corner, right next to the offending bin! So, with sunglasses on, stinking like a winery floor I had to introduce myself to him and then start scrabbling through the bin like a mad woman looking for my birthday presents that I had so deftly disposed of the night before.

All I can remember of that particular moment was him and Jaime, standing and staring – one at her mother and the other at a brand new member of his parish as I finally pulled a bag out of the bin that was full of more booze. The clunking sounds of prosecco and champagne bottles as they exited their bed at night was deafening and I seriously thought, as did Jaime, that this was going to be THE low point of the morning's walk to school. I bid our new vicar a brisk farewell and headed on off to school armed with about 7 bottles of booze.

It was only on our entry into the school playground that my fellow 'night-before-revellers' gave me a bloody round of applause for not only my table dancing but my pole dancing using a beam in the local pub. I was 51.

Jaime said her goodbyes and gaily skipped off into the playground singing

"Oh my god, does anyone want to adopt me???"

Parent of the year did the walk of shame home and sat and cried on the sofa. That is the thing about parental hangovers, the shame! They weren't there, but the fallout always was! No, that was it. I was going to up my game. Tomorrow was a new day, and I was NOT going to get it wrong. Woke up the next morning, absolutely pissing down with rain.

"Right girls, we are NOT walking to school this morning, Mummy is going to drive you in and keep you all warm and dry."

In the car we piled to make the less than a mile journey. Mother of the year is back! But what she has conveniently forgotten is she is still most definitely menopausal and had done her U-turn at the end of the road, got home and sat on the driveway feeling distinctly triumphant. I was back! I had this. My birthday was a one off! Then I heard the little voice behind me

"Mum, we're still in the car..."

Oh dear God.

Chapter 25 - Talk to the animals

And so it went on, I lurched from one domestic and public disaster to the next. School drop offs and pick ups were there for other people's entertainment, so many particular occasions come to mind, mainly they all include my bloody totally untrained Labrador, the infamous Spencer. Things always got more complicated when I offered to look after other people's dogs who just showed up my beast who did whatever the bloody hell he wanted.

Two particular occasions come to mind. One was a lovely black lab who was so docile and well behaved it was embarrassing. I decided to walk the dog with a friend's hound in a different village for a change. We returned to the battle bus, my friend's dog got straight into the boot of the car (he's a good boy) Spencer just sat there and stared at me. What happened next haunts me to this day.

"Spencer, I am going to count to three, if you don't get in on three you are, you are, you are going to go to the vet for an injection!"

Genius. Hates that.

Spencer doesn't move. Looks away, sits there, still as a statue.

"Spencer, I am warning you; Mummy is NOT in the mood for this this morning, get your bastard arse in the feckin car."

Still nothing.

"Spencer, I mean it, this is your last chance, 1... 2... 3... oh FFS, you and I both feckin know you can't count, just get in the fucking car?!"

I do believe, at this moment I actually stamped my welly boot. Things were about to get very serious for Spencer.

Nothing.

Somehow, this gift of a dog has sized me up and has worked out that there is no way I am lifting 40kgs of stubborn labrador into the boot, so we have a standoff. For about 5 minutes.

I do believe I actually had a full on conversation with myself to prove to Spencer that I was not in the slightest bit bothered by his ridiculous behaviour. It starts to rain. Oh really? Oh fuck this for a game of soldiers, this dog is going to be bloody death of me.

"Ok, you little shit bag, you win but no more bloody treats today and NO, you cannot wear Mummy's sodding underwear anymore either!!!"

Put a towel on the back seat of the car. A mud-covered Spencer jumps in, of course NOT on the towel.

"Spencer, you stupid bastard dog, get on the bloody towel! Honestly, anyone would think you do this on feckin purpose you shitbag!"

It was then that I heard the first snigger. I look up to see two, completely hysterical men up two separate ladders mending the church wall. Oh, dear lord, they heard me threatening that the dog couldn't wear my underwear anymore. I want to die. Please please help me find my evaporation button. All I got from one of these lovely ol' boys was,

"Oh my God, I'm gonna fall off this bloody ladder in a minute! Does he really wear your pants?!"

The next was not only a public humiliation but sadly not an isolated incident and indeed a gentle reminder that I should really be in prison.

Taking these two adorable, butter wouldn't melt in their mouths dogglies out, I sensed there was Spencer fodder not far away and for once I was on fire (on this occasion not literally). I smelt the fox shit BEFORE the dog did and saw the bastard head for it. He's pretty quick, but for the first time in months, I had my runners on, and I had this covered. Wading my way like the feckin road runner (ie running like buggery and getting nowhere) I did about 3mph across a beautiful, sun drenched meadow screaming my bloody lungs out

"GET BACK HERE YOU SODDING DOG! YOU ROLL IN THAT MUCK AND I WILL BLOODY KILL YOU SHITBAG MOTHER F******R."

Arms flailing, bingo wings in serious danger of knocking me out, beanbagboobs doing something that resembled an out of control windmill and then it happened.

A sweet, dear little family walking towards me as I was still in full tilt of this strange running/seizure type thing swearing at the top of my voice -

"SPENCER YOU ARE ONE FECKIN DEAD DOG IF YOU EAT THAT SHIT OR BLOODY ROLL IN IT, I AM IN SODDING CHARGE HERE YOU INSOLENT, DISRESPECTFUL TOTALLY UNTRAINED FECKER"

It was only when I spotted them that the perfectly shaped tree root, an arch with a little sticky outy bit, got stuck to my trainer and down went the large, sweary, batshit crazy totally out of control dog owner. My friend's dog was running obediently by my side the whole time.I slowly look up, the family in question are within metres of this god awful spectacle and the father has his hands actually over the little boy's ears. It turns out that it is really quite difficult to apologise when you have a mouthful of mud, grass and a stray dandelion, but attempt it I did and whilst trying to regain a vertical stature, Spencer decided THAT was the precise moment to prove his dominance over me and began humping the hell out of my enormous rear end and the whole situation got substantially worse.

The family scuttled off as fast as they could, and it was only then that I realised that not only had my bastard dog rolled in fox shit but so had I.

Chapter 26 - Nailed it! *Not*

As I hurtled towards my 51st birthday, I realised that I really did have to start finding my place in this mad world and with the road safety job sadly coming to an end due to a lack of funding, I found myself beholden to two extra things that I am truly crap at. One, decision making and two, the possibility that I MIGHT end up having to be a bloody housewife.

Now, do NOT get me wrong, there is absolutely nothing wrong with being a housewife. In fact, I would like it strictly noted that I have the greatest respect and am in total awe of anyone, man or woman who makes the extraordinarily brave decision to be one. It is the ultimate in thankless, selfless multi-tasking. I know this because I tried it for a week. Eddie said, when we received the news that my days of delivering workshops (often with my dog beside me) to the emergency services and young drivers were over,

"Why don't you be a stay at home wife and mother for a while, my love, you have worked since Jaime started school, now you can just work for me."

It was the last bit of that sentence I should have listened a tad more carefully to when I accepted my new employment but nevertheless, I threw myself into the vocation with some vigour. My day started with the school run which invariably involved several journeys backwards and forwards as it turns out my daughters were more forgetful than me. I recall one particular occasion when Jaime called me from her secondary school announcing that for the second time that week, she had forgotten her PE kit. And for the second time that week I jumped back in my taxi and raced into reception only to discover that I TOO had forgotten her feckin PE kit. So that was three 10 mile round trips. Stay at home Mummy thing NOT going too well so far.

So back home, I need a coffee and a sit down after all that driving and apologising to the school receptionist.

Silence.

Ooooh, I don't know about this. Silence and no particular direction to my day. Where to begin. What to do? Undecided as to whether I was deeply comfortable with this new emptiness of no compass, no diary, no "to-do" list or the polar opposite. In order to distract myself from this dilemma I put on the goggle box, something which I hadn't done since my teenage years – TV in the morning! But like vodka on the cornflakes, only actually more addictive as ol' Jezza Kyle came on! Bugger me, there really were people out there with more shagged out lives than mine! I had had some weird shit happen to me, but I had never had a dalliance with my cousin or certainly not with any of my Dad's mates.

It was like a bloody drug! To this day, I am trying to work out, for me personally anyway, if it was pure voyeurism or just a truly simplified way to make my world seem vaguely normal, innocent at least. Either way, two hours of my new job had been totally and utterly wasted by several people forgetting the same PE kit and then one of them watching people screaming blue murder at each other for fornicating with relatives for people like me to gawp at.

Ok, what next? Oh god, there was no escaping walking the hound. This was going to be simplified by taking him much more locally and more remotely so that hopefully he could just ablute and have a run around and all incognito. Job done. All good. Now, what was my job description exactly? I had never done this before.

I had been a single mother to two small tikes which basically involved becoming one of them for a few hours, jigsaw puzzles and playing at princesses then to get wrapped up in some or another inane CBeebies TV programme, lunch, clear up lunch and then some kind of outdoor activity which then was always followed by cleaning up copious amounts of mud from every single part of both the children and then the house.

Your day would then suddenly speed up right about the time when for the last 30 years it had actually started to come to a delightful drifting stop, around 5ish, or the 'witching hours' as I had come to call them.

These were the busiest and most chaotic parts of the day which included making tea, breaking up a fight, putting out the fire because you have turned your back on making the tea, breaking up another fight, dishing up tea, breaking up third fight which has entailed the throwing of said tea at each other or tipping it over each other's heads. Cleaning up the tea. Another fight breaks out, you really can't be arsed to break this one up, if they kill each other, blame the previous fire. Run the bath, throw them in the bath. Get drenched. Get them out of the bath. Break up another fight. Clean the 4" of water off the bathroom floor and then story time when you are actually ready to enter full murder mode.

You either scream the bedtime or at least say it through gritted teeth and then you say the most ridiculous and meaningless words that every mother of small children says and knows full well mean fuck all,

"Goodnight my little ones – and here they come – SEE YOU IN THE MORNING"

Of course, you see them at least 14 times after saying that.

Separately.

Then it's time to WINE down.

And this my friends, is why most mothers of small children, are in fact functioning alcoholics. It's the only way to actually have a mood change, be an adult again, be who you once were again. Or at the very least live in the la la land that you ARE still who you once were.

I digress. I am now a fully-fledged ME, only with a really important job as a housewife. With not a fucking clue where to start or what to do.

It is now 11am and I have done sweet FA and with only 4 hours left before the second disaster of a school run starts, I need to get my arse into gear.

Washing. Things need washing! In it all goes. Round and round the machine goes and all is well with the world. Then the doorbell rings. Van pulls up.

Doorbell rings again. Spencer naturally assumes the caller is for him, springs into action, ready to race out the front door and cause mayhem. I look down, I have trousers on. All is good. Grab the hound. Get the fecker tucked inside the front door. Open the front door. There stands Sussex's answer to Tom Hardy.

Our eyes meet, he smiles, oh dear god he smiles, I smile back. Then it happens. Spencer lets off what could possibly be mistaken for the 4 minute fucking warning. It is not short, it is not sweet, it is long, tuneful, it tapers off and then races into a musical crescendo and then... silence... and one last trumpet blast.

It only now occurs to me that Tom Hardy and I have not actually broken eye contact throughout this brass section solo from my dog's arse. The silence is pure and utter sodding agony. But I will NOT be beaten by this brutish feckin hound, I will NOT! This time, I will use my gumption and my instinct, and I will tell this beautiful man that that noise had absolutely NOTHING to do with me and was all down to my bastard labrador who was hiding behind the door.

"Oh my God, oh my God, I am SOOOOOOO sorry. That wasn't me, that was my dog..."

He smiles again. Oh, mother of god, I am going to melt into this man's arms soon.

"Sure, they all say that."

Then there is the sexiest little snigger, and he turns to go.

No no no, I will not have this! Spencer, you are NOT ruining another beautiful moment for me and this GOD!

"No, no, I am serious, look here he is!"

And by some small miracle Spencer senses that I need his help after his revolting show of excitement about an Amazon delivery, and races out of the door. Tom strokes and ruffles Spencer's hair and calls him a 'good boy' and all that jazz.

"So you see, it WAS the dog, it WAS you boy, wasn't it?"

I'd love to be able to show you the "Really?" look that I got, but it was far too sexy for words so I will just give you the words,

"What's he gonna do eh? Say, yes sir it was me that made that unbelievable sound?"

"Well, no, of course he's not."

I am panicking now, and this is NEVER a good thing,

"He's a dog and of course he can't speak, but there will be evidence, I can prove it..."

And here it came. It just fell out of my totally unreliable, completely off the chart monstrous and always out of control gob,

"There'll be a scorch mark or something..."

There's that silence again.

"Oh shit fuck bollocks, I just said that outloud didn't I?"

"Yes you did (looks down) Mrs Emma...."

And he was gone. Gone to the sea of all other delivery drivers that have come before him. I wonder if, they talk about the infamous, feral, totally unfeminine farting female who blames everything on her fucking dog. Shit fuck bollocks. Blown it. He could well be a regular visitor to my new workplace and now he just thinks I am a middle aged woman with no control of her wind regulation. Glare at the bloody dog. He will be the end of me.

But I can do this. Generations of women before me and many others amongst me have looked after homes and families since time immemorial. It can't be bloody rocket science! I hear a few beeps.

The washing machine has finished. I have had far too much coffee in the interim and spent far too much time on the phone to my friends. But I am embracing my position with vigour and pull myself off the caffeine ceiling and open the washing machine door. Absolutely EVERYTHING is pink.

I was only given a few initial instructions by my new employer, my husband, and was, most emphatically, NOT to mix whites with coloureds. So how the buggery had this happened. I pull out all his brand new pink shirts to find a random red sock lurking at the back of the bastard machine.

Oh, you little shit. How the HELL did you get in there? I am so fucked. This is one of the beloved's pet hates. I have to move on though, time is ticking on and all I have achieved so far is to get the answers to a lie detector test wrong on both occasions, humiliate myself in front of the Amazon driver, solve a few problems for my mates on the phone and change the colour of my husband's entire work wardrobe. NOT quite the start I was aiming for, but in retrospect, possibly inevitable.

Dinner next. Yes, dinner. What the bloody hell was for dinner? How on earth did I used to do all this when I was working? Look in the fridge – unless they wanted black olives with some butter and a mouldy piece of cheese, I was pretty screwed so off to the supermarket I head.

It's a strange feeling, and it's even stranger describing it to you as a strange feeling that going to the supermarket as part of your working day rather than just slipping out to do "a quick dash shop for tea" but it is. You sort of feel free. So free in fact that you have forgotten absolutely bloody everything from your bags for life, to the shopping list oh, and as it turns out, your handbag. Back home again, grab everything that used to come so naturally and leisurely I cruised around Tesco with not a care in the world. Just a housewife doing her thing, caring for her family and buying all the provisions we all needed so that life was like something out of a 1950's advert.

Slipping over in the milk aisle was par for the course really, to be expected. I got to the checkout to discover that one of my bastard kids had taken my card out to buy something off Amazon and I was suddenly holding up a load of seriously professional looking housewives with no means of payment whatsoever. This had not happened to me before, so I had no idea what to do. Do they just let you go and hope you do the honourable thing and come back with your card? Oh no. Customer services are shouted for, lights are flashing all over the tills and you are almost under armed guard and shepherded over to the security desk and asked to leave your full trolley there, head home, get some money to actually PAY for your provisions and then return and queue up again.

FFS.

This was the second time today I had done a third journey home from a simple job. I get back to Tesco, pay for my goods and drive home. Pretty close to tears at this point as I realise that this is not for the fainthearted. When the tears really DID start to fall was arriving home with all my frozen stuff melted and leaking all over the boot, there were Jaime and Abbie standing at the front door with one of my best friends who had tried to get hold of me without success as of course I had also forgotten to take my phone with me and had also forgotten to do the second part of the school run – the picking up part.

I got out of the car totally mortified and dissolved into a big mess on the doorstep whilst the kids thought it was ace as my friend was the mother to their two best mates and so a "treat tea" which involved a bottle of wine or three was in order and the desperate realisation that I was going to be utterly shit at this job and something had to change. Eddie came home to a half drunk, tearful wife and a load of strawberry milkshake coloured shirts and a letter of resignation. I had lasted all of one day in my new job. I will NEVER EVER underestimate the skill, talent and composure of those of you who ARE stay at home mums and wives. It's no mean feat to keep it all together and I had really done absolutely nothing but managed to fuck even that up!

So, to find a job. Hmmm...

Chapter 27 - The reality, the light

The trouble with doing a job that you are crap at by default whilst looking for another job is that you are constantly picking up the pieces of your current occupation whilst trying to boost your confidence to step even further out of your comfort zone after being a) A Sales Manager in print (most of life) b) failed wife c) single mother d) road safety officer e) failed housewife, mother and general dogsbody. Lots of "failed " in there. But there is the double-edged sword, I needed something to get me out of this mess I had managed to get both my family and myself into, that being, me in charge of running our family home. Starvation, various water borne diseases and divorce were all imminent. Something had to be done. So, the job search began with a vengeance.

My first interview came through after making just two phone calls. I was thrilled. Receptionist at a local care home. Just up the road, answer the phone, meet and greet the relatives of the inmates, sorry, inhabitants (can you see where I may have come unstuck here within LESS than a day?) So fortunately, on arrival in the lobby of the care home, I tripped up on a piece of upturned carpet, wiped out an enormous plant and sent the whole lot flying across the immaculate reception area and spent what should have been my interview on my hands and knees with a dustpan and brush and sadly my swear filter broke at this point and the job interview was over before it even started.

The family were all very supportive, the excessive laughter was a little much for me to bear at that stage, but not one to be deterred from "fate and destiny" I buggered on with the job ads until I came across another interesting job which was local and extremely interesting. A photographic company who needed a PA. Love a bit of photography and who knows, maybe the odd celebrity might pop in and make my day.

Wore different shoes to this interview and was bustled in by the photographer's wife who took one look at me and decided instantly that she hated me despite my attempts to convince her I was perfect for the job. To my utter disbelief, after half an hour of general chat about my past, my present and my hopes, dreams and wishes, I was offered the job on the spot!

Unbefuckinglieveable! I was to start the following Monday and the first job was to accompany the photographer to a field shoot as his assistant which entailed 3 hours in a car with him, holding all his kit and making sure people stood in the right places and the lighting was correct, 3 hours in the car back with him and then having his tongue shoved firmly down the back of my throat on the return back to the studio.

Another one had bitten the dust.

Back to the drawing board.

It's at moments like this, when you are menopausal, mid-life, kids growing fast, second marriage and although everything looks bloody perfect on paper, you find yourself utterly lost.

Who am I?
Who was I?
Who do I want to be?

I knew I couldn't go back to sales, I had done my time on that one, and trust me there is a whole other book in that story! So, scrap that. Could I give being a housewife, the controller of everyone's happiness and comfort (because that is what it entails) – after 8 hours of attempting it, I had proven that I needed something else to occupy this insane mind to keep it altogether, so no. Not an option.

Back to working in a pub? The only real option there was our local where I had not only been disgraced by my dog on numerous occasions but also let myself down pretty badly too. No, I think most of my fellow villagers would have just assumed I was the entertainment rather than ACTUAL staff so that was a nonstarter. So, what?

Time for a chat with myself.

I am 52 years old.

I have a somewhat sketchy education.

I have done some seriously "out there" jobs, from being a rather unreliable hostie on a racing yacht serving tea and coffee at a 90 degree angle and falling in on a regular basis, to direct marketing for a sex toy manufacturer on the streets of Sydney – and yes, I tried to demonstrate how the bastard thing worked by inserting into my mouth and chipping most of my teeth, to some serious occupations such as Sales Management and as I have previously mentioned, road safety for young people.

In short, I have tried my hand at pretty much everything. But, and here it is, the end of this book, auto-biography, diary – whatever you would like to call it, NOTHING has come close to writing my blog, The Menopausal Mayhem Mothers on Instagram and Facebook. Nothing could touch the heart-warming messages I have received from you all who have told me that on your darkest days, I have made you smile, even laugh.

I set out writing this book with a totally different intention.

To write a book.

End of.

But it turns out that writing a book like this should be about making a difference to someone's day, someone's week, someone's year. It should be memorable and moving. I hope that anyone who has taken the time and trouble to read this will be somehow inspired that even with the darkest of starts, comes light at the end of that long tunnel – there will a few small trains that will run you over, but you WILL get back up because, for no other reason, why the fuck not? Why lie there, in a dark tunnel, waiting for the next train?

If something mortifying but not deadly or tragic happens to you and you have the option to laugh at it, LAUGH! You are only laughing at yourself and how hilarious that moment will feel in an hour or so's time. If you are hit with tragedy, such as the death of a loved one, remember that grief and heartache, even the worst kind, is the price we pay for deep deep love. Some people go through life without feeling anything for anyone. People are simply assets to them, even their own children. They may not feel the pain of heartbreak or loss, but they will also never know the joy of pure love and all the magic that that brings.

Laughter, disaster, excruciating embarrassment and LOVE are what makes us human, and I think, personally, we should not only be proud that we have experienced all these, but we should revel in them, roll deliciously in them, celebrate them and tell the world about them. Because, as life has taught me, you are here for a great time, not a long time and when all's said and done, be remembered for all the right reasons. When you leave this mortal coil, be mourned for the hole you leave in people's hearts because you made them feel better about themselves by being YOU.

Thank you for taking the time and trouble to read this. I have loved writing it.

Spencer and I are off now. More fox shit. More foliage. More disasters.

Until next time x

THE END (FOR NOW...)

Printed in Great Britain
by Amazon